D0251251

FLOOD FORECAST

for Janet

who cares about
these matters
with respect and
thanks

R W Sandford

FLOOD FORECAST

Climate Risk and Resiliency in Canada

ROBERT WILLIAM SANDFORD
AND KERRY FREEK

Rocky Mountain Books
www.rmbooks.com

Library and Archives Canada Cataloguing in Publication

Sandford, Robert W., author
Flood forecast : climate risk and resiliency in Canada / Robert William Sandford and Kerry Freek.

Includes bibliographical references.
Issued in print and electronic formats.
ISBN 978-1-77160-004-0 (bound).—
ISBN 978-1-77160-005-7 (html).—
ISBN 978-1-77160-006-4 (pdf)

1. Floods—Ontario—Toronto. 2. Floods—Alberta—Calgary. 3. Flood forecasting—Canada. 4. Climatic changes—Canada. I. Freek, Kerry, author II. Title.

GB1399.5.C3S36 2014 551.48'90971 C2013-908260-3
C2013-908261-1

Printed in Canada

Rocky Mountain Books acknowledges the financial support for its publishing program from the Government of Canada through the Canada Book Fund (CBF) and the Canada Council for the Arts, and from the province of British Columbia through the British Columbia Arts Council and the Book Publishing Tax Credit.

The interior pages of this book have been produced on 100% post-consumer recycled paper, processed chlorine free and printed with vegetable-based dyes.

For my sister Margaret,
who lost so much in the flood

— ROBERT WILLIAM SANDFORD

To Canada's hardworking water stewards,
for their inspiring resiliency

— KERRY FREEK

Contents

Acknowledgements

R.W. Sandford:

This is one of those rare books that emerge in real time out of dramatic, generation-shaping events that alter the lives of those that experience them. Fortunately, more than a dozen researchers from the Centre for Hydrology at the University of Saskatchewan happened to be in the Canmore and Kananaskis area when the flooding began in June of 2013. These highly qualified scientists shared minute-by-minute, hour-by-hour observations of the hydrological conditions and physical changes they studied in real time as floodwaters overwhelmed their instruments and might have threatened their lives had they not been trained to deal with such hazards.

This book could not have been written without the direct support of Dr. John Pomeroy of the University of Saskatchewan and the members of his research team, who generously shared both time and information during the flood and throughout the months that followed. Dr. Pomeroy's team includes Dr. Kevin Shook, Paul Whitfield, May Guan, Angus Duncan, Xing Fang, Dr. Keith Musselman, Dhiraj Pradhananga and Nicholas Leroux. Responsibility for errors, omissions, misperceptions or misunderstandings, however, resides solely with the author.

I would also like to acknowledge the enormous and very timely support of Don Gorman, Joe Wilderson and Chyla Cardinal of RMB | Rocky Mountain Books in the production of this contribution to the RMB Manifesto Series.

And of course, I wish to thank my family for their courage, patience and support, not only in dealing with the flood and its impacts on Canmore but also in managing the event's significant personal, professional and political consequences.

Kerry Freek:

First, a sincere thanks to Bob Sandford for willingly sharing with me his initial and unfolding thoughts on the Alberta flood, and, when the events in Toronto hit, convincing Don Gorman and the RMB | Rocky Mountain Books team to allow me to participate in this documentation. Bob is truly a force of nature, and his dedication to improving water management in Canada is nothing short of inspiring.

Thank you to all the experts I depended on during my term as editor of *Water Canada*. Many of these people spent valuable time sharing their wisdom, knowledge and opinions. They have truly helped build the publication from the ground up, and I consider myself lucky that many of those experts have also become great friends.

Conversations with Penny Beames, Randall Blom, Vivien Fellegi, Blair Feltmate, Nancy Goucher, Abe Khademi, John Kinkead, Carolyn Lee, Carol Moffatt, Mark Ortiz, Bruce Pardy, Lee Scarlett, Mira Shenker, Wendy Smith, Krystyn Tully, Christine Zimmer and many other friends and water warriors informed this project, and I'm grateful for their support and patience.

Some of the material included here first appeared in *Water Canada* and is used with the permission of the magazine's proud publisher, Todd Latham.

Thank you also to my family.

Introduction

All you have to do is open a newspaper, surf the web or turn on the television and you realize that the world is changing. There is a growing sense in Canada and abroad that there is something terribly wrong out there, and that it is way bigger than just our current global economic woes. Whatever it is, it is coming at us fast and it looks like it is connected to water.

Water responds directly to climate. Liquid water, snow and ice respond directly, visibly and measurably to temperature. If we follow what is happening to our water, it will tell us what is happening to our climate. The long-term impacts of the loss of glacier ice and changes in the extent and duration of snowcover, and how that affects the amount of water our streams and rivers contain, is becoming better understood. We have known for some time that groundwater and surface water are really the same thing. We also know that streamflows are diminishing in the western part of the Canadian prairies. The cascading effects of diminished streamflow on fragile aquatic ecosystems are also becoming better understood. These include changes in water chemistry and temperature which result in changes in the species of diatoms in the water, which in turn impact every niche in the food chain, right up through insects to the kinds of fish that can exist in various cold-water conditions.

The connection between water and climate becomes more controversial, however, when you talk about what is happening at the nexus of water and climate. Increases in the frequency of extreme weather events are generating flood conditions and debris torrents that are resulting in abrupt landscape change. Such events have also begun to damage our cities. With a warming climate we can expect extreme weather events to occur more frequently and landscape change to accelerate.

In parts of Canada – and particularly in the West – this is not something that is discussed openly, however. You can elaborate on long-term water-related geological processes all you want.

But the moment you move from water to climate circumstances in the immediate term, you are immediately confronted with resistance to the mere mention of climate warming and – from some quarters – vigorous and outright denial of any human influence whatsoever on what are clearly natural climate cycles. While nothing ruins a pleasant dinner party conversation more than a fist fight, at a certain point these matters become hard to duck. At the time of this writing we had already been told five times, in increasingly certain terms, that the world is warming and we humans are warming it.

The first time we were told this was in 1990 when a report published by the newly formed Intergovernmental Panel on Climate Change announced that the phenomenon was real and that it could have huge impact on future generations.

The second time we were told was when the Second Assessment Report was published five years later. In addition to presenting the science behind claims that climate change was indeed a fact, this report calmly illuminated the potential economic and social ramifications of the problem.

The Third Assessment Report, published in

2001, told us again that there was a sound physical-science basis for concerns over climate change and that the world was vulnerable to a wide range of impacts if it did not mitigate the effects of greenhouse gases on the composition and behaviour of our planet's atmosphere.

The fourth time we were told was in 2007. We were told again in 2013.

In a manner consistent with the highest ideals of science, IPCC reports bear the stamp of the highest possible standards of research rigour and objectivity. As a result of three full years of carefully interpreting the research outcomes funded by the Canadian Foundation for Climate and Atmospheric Science, I appreciate the scientific method more than ever and confidently trust the conclusions of this report. The scientific method is highly demanding. It is a given that every time another scientist challenges any aspect of contemporary climate science – and this happens continually – researchers are forced by the long-established conventions of the method to take that challenge seriously. Even when known deniers and outright cranks contest any aspect of the growing body of climate science, researchers are bound by the scientific method to subject that challenge to thorough, objective analysis of its relevance in the context of everything we presently know about the matter in question. This is how science advances over time. On matters related to climate we have been doing this for forty years.

The IPCC Fifth Assessment Report provides the clearest view yet of the current state of scientific knowledge about climate change. A total of 209 lead authors, together with 50 review editors from 39 countries and more than 600 contributing authors from 32 countries, assisted in preparing just the "Working Group I" section in the Fifth Assessment. That group alone sorted through and addressed 54,677 critical comments in preparing their report. Two other working groups will have done the same. The results are significant. What has happened once more is that after running objections again and again through the entire body of climate change knowledge we keep arriving back at the same conclusions.

The global thermometer, it appears, is as indifferent to the psychological tricks of advertising and unrelenting public relations as it is to economic theory. The temperature readings keep coming in, and no matter how many times we check them, the picture that is forming of our circumstances and our future doesn't change. Our world is warming up, and at the moment at least, it looks like it is going to warm up a lot more, with consequences for everything that matters about where and how we live today. Five times we have been told. Maybe it is time to listen.

You can create your own physics – or dismiss physics or even deny science altogether – but you can't change these facts: we are altering the composition of our atmosphere, and the effects this is having on water are becoming hard to ignore. Our hydro-climatic circumstances are changing. While the clearest evidence of these changes is in the Arctic, there is also clear evidence of hydro-climatic change in the Canadian West.

If you were in southern Manitoba and Saskatchewan in 2011, or with Kerry Freek in Toronto in 2013, you will know that hydro-climatic change is no longer an abstract idea or theoretical concept when it comes after you or threatens your life and livelihood. Because it is so topical – and because it affected me, my family and many of my friends and neighbours so very personally – it is even more important to explain what we currently know about hydro-climate change by way of the disastrous flooding that took place at Canmore and downstream in Calgary and southern Alberta in June of 2013.

The purpose of this book is to explore what we can learn from science and from recent events that will help us enhance community resilience to accelerating hydro-climatic change in Canada. Humanity has been dealing with flooding since the birth of civilization. We already knew a great deal about the vulnerability of cities to flooding long before we made fossil fuels our energy source of choice.

Obviously, scientists already had a pretty good understanding of the effect of rising atmospheric temperatures on the global hydrological cycle long before the great Alberta flood of 2013. Hydrologists had long predicted the return intervals of floods under constant climate and had shown that much larger floods than had been experienced in most people's lifetime were certain to occur. It was also known that climate change would likely affect the probability of these floods. While no scientist has formally tied the Alberta floods to changing climate in a rigorous study, it is suggested as a likely hypothesis but needs careful study to establish. It took ten years for British scientists to relate the floods of 2000 to changing climate. The same link to climate change, however, has been identified in terms of the massive flooding that was taking place in England at the time of this writing in early 2014. Even without a clearly identified link between flooding and climate change in Canada, enough was known about the nature and dynamics of increasingly destructive weather that researchers had already predicted that it was only a matter of time before a big storm in the Rocky Mountains would generate major flooding in mountain communities upstream of Calgary and in neighbouring communities in adjacent watersheds.

For at least a decade, hydrologists not just in Canada but worldwide have been reporting changes in the rate and manner in which water moves through the global hydrological cycle. It is probably safe to say, however, that very few of even the most far-seeing researchers were able to recognize just how serious those consequences might be. Long before Alberta woke up to the threat, changes in the way the global hydrological cycle functions were already beginning to test the resilience of the global economic system, the adaptability of business and the flexibility of governments around the world. There remains, however, a huge gap between awareness of these problems and the amount of policy attention they receive.

Each year, the World Economic Forum evaluates the 50 global economic, environmental, geopolitical, societal and technological issues of concern in the immediate and long term. In 2012 the Forum ranked water-related issues fifth in terms of their likelihood of slowing economic performance globally. In 2013 the growing global hydro-climatic crisis was ranked fourth among threats generally, but second in terms of its potential to affect not just the performance but the very survival of businesses in many sectors of the global economy. What we are beginning to see is that hydro-climatic change is colliding head-on with an already troubled economic status quo. Many of the connected hydro-climatic effects that threaten the global economy have been identified.

First, a link appears to exist between ocean temperatures and how much sea ice there is in the

Arctic. There is also a connection between how much snowcover there is continentally and soil moisture. And it appears that all of these factors in tandem affect the stability of the high-altitude band of winds, called the jet stream, which circulates around the northern hemisphere. There also appears to be a link between a meandering jet stream and the movement of warm and cold fronts into places where they don't often go and don't normally stay. It is this loss of stability that causes abnormal winter cold snaps with accompanying record lows to persist in surprising places, as well as record-high temperatures at high latitudes such as the +12°C recently recorded in Canada's Yukon Territory in January. The loss of the stability of the jet stream may ultimately be of concern to all of us because it is this emerging pattern that appears to be causing heat waves and droughts to persist far longer and more widely.

Secondly, we know from a very simple principle of atmospheric physics that a warmer atmosphere can transport more water vapour. This simple fact in itself results in the potential for heavier rainfalls.

And finally, all of these factors together are creating more frequent and more intense flooding events. As we saw in southern Alberta and Toronto in 2013 these elements of hydro-climatic change will have implications for public policy throughout the Canadian West and, as Kerry Freek will explain, implications for urban planning, not just in Toronto but in every city in North America now and in the future.

PART ONE: ALBERTA

... ten thousand River Commissions, with the mines of the world at their back, cannot tame that lawless stream, cannot curb it or confine it, cannot say to it Go here, or Go there, and make it obey; cannot save a shore which it has sentenced; cannot bar its path with an obstruction which it will not tear down, dance over, and laugh at.

— MARK TWAIN,
Life on the Mississippi (1883)

Curiously, the most important climate feedbacks all involve water, in either its solid, liquid, or gas form.

— JAMES HANSEN,
Storms of My Grandchildren (2009)

Following the water

Because it is so central to understanding what the floods in Alberta and elsewhere in Canada in 2013 mean to our future, it is important to explore more fully just what we know about our changing hydro-climatic circumstances. If you want to solve a crime or bust a bad bank, it is conventional wisdom that you follow the money. If you want to find out what is causing more-extreme weather events, you follow the water. To that end, it is important to identify key elements of the global hydrological cycle and follow the movement of water through that cycle. In so doing, we discover that water in the form of snow and ice plays a much larger role in determining global climatic conditions than many ever thought.

One of the most significant recent advancements in hydro-meteorology is the realization of how globally important the refrigerating influence of polar sea ice is. Three factors related to the extent and duration of Arctic sea ice have emerged as having great significance to the lives of every person on this planet. The first is the amount of heat required to melt sea-ice. The second is the potential effect of sea ice melt on ocean acidification and the reliability of deep ocean currents. The third is the profound influence of Arctic cold on the stability of weather conditions farther south and globally.

Water is an almost otherworldly substance. Once it is frozen it takes an enormous amount of heat to weaken the hydrogen bonds that hold water molecules in the rigid crystalline structure of ice. The amount of energy required to melt 1 kilogram of ice that is already at 0°C is equivalent to the amount of energy required to raise the temperature of 1 kilogram of liquid water by 79°C (the boiling point of water is 100°C). From this we see why ice and snow are such effective climatic refrigerants. The problem, however, is that the moment after solid ice collapses into liquid water, all the heat you add afterwards will suddenly raise temperatures and increase evaporation.

Polar ice is now seen as a thermostat that

governs major weather patterns globally. It is now feared that the decrease in the extent and thickness of sea ice could be the parameter that is feeding all of the increases that are causing concern over climate change. While there is annual variability in how much ice disappears each year, the area of Arctic sea ice that melted in 2012 was nearly the equivalent of the area of Canada as a landmass.

Sea ice is a thermal helmet without which climate warming can give the Earth system a shot straight to the head. If we lose the refrigerating influence of Arctic sea ice, global temperatures will skyrocket, with possible releases of methane from the permafrost zone that will further exacerbate warming. As I will point out later, evidence from Siberia suggests this may already be happening.

The loss of Arctic sea ice and the reduction of the extent and duration of snowcover in the northern hemisphere are reducing the temperature gradient between the pole and the tropics. It is this difference in temperature between the polar region and the warmer air to the south that largely defines the behaviour of the jet stream.

Observations of the jet stream have revealed that warmer atmospheric temperatures do not automatically translate into warmer weather. In a uniformly warmer and therefore more turbulent atmosphere, both warm and cold fronts end up and persist in places in the mid-latitudes where they were not common in the past, as mentioned earlier. Changes in atmospheric circulation patterns are pushing major subtropical storm tracks toward the poles, often causing floods of magnitudes we are poorly equipped to manage. This is also why we are seeing more – and more widespread – droughts and wildfires followed by major floods in the same river basins in the same year. "Come hell *and* high water," if you will.

What we are also seeing is not uniform warming but the destabilization of historical weather patterns. People all around the world are complaining that the weather is all over the place, and they're right: it *is* all over the place. Two years before the great floods in Canada in 2013, we believe we already knew why such extremes of weather appeared to be becoming more frequent.

Recent research has clearly demonstrated that in the Arctic and throughout much of the Canadian boreal, the quantity of water that had been trapped as sea ice and in glaciers, permanent snowpack and permafrost is in rapid decline. What is happening in the Arctic and in the North is exactly what is happening is much of the rest of Canada. Warming is causing the post-glacial hydrological wealth of Canada to change form. The water is not disappearing, however. Water doesn't do that. What is happening is that frozen water and liquid water are moving to different places in the hydrosphere: permanent ice and snow are becoming liquid water, and liquid water is evaporating. This is going to add additional edge to the already existing natural variability that characterizes weather and climate here and in much of the rest of Canada.

As I pointed out in my earlier book *Saving Lake Winnipeg*, the same warming that is causing permafrost to thaw in the North, glaciers to disappear in our western mountains and precipitation patterns on the prairies to change is also causing water left on the land after the last glaciation to evaporate. Research conducted at the University of Maryland demonstrates that lakes in northern Canada lost 6700 square kilometres of surface area, or roughly one-third of the area of Lake Ontario. Increasing evaporation also appears to be reducing water levels in the Great Lakes. So where is all this missing water going?

One of the places it is going is into the atmosphere, where it becomes available to fuel more frequent and intense extreme weather events. We are seeing this right across Canada as well as in Europe and elsewhere in the northern hemisphere. The algorithm upon which this assertion rests is one of the most basic principles in atmospheric physics: warmer air holds more water. The amount of water the atmosphere can hold increases by about 7 per cent per degree Celsius, or about 4 per cent per degree Fahrenheit. So what's the problem? The problem is that our entire built and agricultural environment, including urban water supply systems, stormwater infrastructure, roads, bridges and farms, are all designed for an earlier, more stable climate. These matters were already being discussed all over Canada long before the flooding occurred in Alberta.

Eight months before the flood: October 15–19, 2012

In October of 2012 the University of Regina and the University of Texas at Austin, in association with the North China Electric Power University and the United Nations Water for Life Decade Partnership in Canada, hosted a major international conference around the theme "Storm Warning: Water, Energy and Climate Security in a Changing World." The conference was held in Banff, Alberta, which provided an opportunity for a field trip that allowed participants to experience the spectacular Canadian Rocky Mountains and see through the eyes of experts what warming mean annual temperatures are doing to glaciers, snowpack and snowcover in Banff and Jasper national parks.

The invitation-only conference drew some seventy experts from the United States, Canada, Japan, China, Australia and Thailand to address six sources of significant uncertainty that will affect water, energy and climate security in the coming decades of the 21st century. Among other things, participants discussed what is known and what remains unknown about fluctuations in water availability and climate before and after the influence of human activity; and what can and cannot be learned from models or forecasts of climate based on "downscaling" from the global to the local, as well as insufficiently articulated feedback loops and other second-order effects. Experts also outlined what is known and not known about the real costs of adaptation to extreme climate events. Also on the agenda were ways in which global, regional and local governance systems and legal regimes adapt to uncertainty in water availability and climate fluctuations.

The Storm Warning conference proceedings made it clear that our climate is changing in profound ways and that the causes of these changes are not natural, but anthropogenic: that humans are now a force affecting the global climate. It was held that this fact in itself constituted the urgency of issuing a global climate change storm warning.

Researchers demonstrated that a warming climate is not going to change the amount of water in the world, but it will change how much of it is found in which state at any given time in the larger, global hydrological cycle. Better understanding of where and how water might move differently through the cycle under warmer conditions will require better hydro-climatic modelling.

It was also made clear at the conference that one of the most immediate and obvious ways climate change is affecting humanity is through the impacts extreme weather events are having on large cities. It was noted that even the most developed countries will face significant challenges in dealing with manifold climate effects, especially as they relate to costly urban flooding. In this context, groundwater overdraft with consequent land subsidence, combined with dense development in flood plains and rising sea levels, have begun to contribute significantly to the growing vulnerability of many major urban areas, not just in Asia but around the world. The magnitude of insured and uninsured losses associated with such flooding is becoming a major societal liability, especially in already crowded flood-prone regions. Liability issues associated with these effects are already increasing insurance rates and even affecting the availability of insurance in high-risk areas globally.

Participants in the conference were shown how major urban centres like Toronto have developed advanced tools for monitoring, managing and adapting to climate effects. These effects, however, appear to be intensifying and now require serious attention, not just for reasons of public health and safety but because the failure to effectively manage floods has been shown to undermine public confidence in government and its institutions. The North York area of Toronto experienced eight extreme events in only 20 years. Stormwater infrastructure in Toronto was designed to manage 1 in 25 year return events. The city's plumbing is not designed to withstand storms of this magnitude and higher, which are occurring more frequently, resulting in major flooding in some parts of the city.

It was made clear that changes in the hydrological cycle are undermining traditional approaches to managing urban water infrastructure. There is a crucial need to assess the cost of adapting versus the costs we should expect to bear if we don't adapt. The magnitude of the problem is enormous and budgets are limited. Raising infrastructure design standards in response to changing climatic conditions, however, is not easy to do anywhere. Public and political resistance to making more money available to deal with these matters is deep and substantial. There are also matters of equity that must be taken into account. On one hand is the huge cost of retrofitting whole neighbourhoods to higher standards. On the other loom the class action lawsuits that have been threatened or pursued against municipalities by citizens whose property suffers repeated flooding as a consequence of outmoded infrastructure design standards. Unfortunately, until we know how much global warming will occur and what consequences to expect, appropriate infrastructure design standards will remain a moving target.

Two weeks after the Storm Warning conference was held in Canada, Hurricane Sandy, in combination with other highly unusual weather, hammered much of the northeastern seaboard of the United States. High winds and rain combined with high tides to create storm surges that flooded many coastal cities, including New York. The effects underscored all of the concerns expressed at the conference regarding the vulnerability of mega-cities everywhere in the world to more frequent and more intense extreme weather events.

Two months before: Wednesday, April 24, 2013

The British Columbia Water and Waste Association held its 41st annual conference and trade show in Kelowna from April 20 to 24, 2013. The final day featured a seminar entitled

"Not Waiting for Noah: New Approaches to Assessing Flood Risk." A dozen speakers ranging from engineers, municipal managers, provincial water policy experts and agricultural specialists joined real estate and insurance professionals in speaking out on what they thought ought to be done to address the growing threat to the British Columbia economy caused by a combination of more-extreme weather events and sea level rise.

Robert Laing of the BC Real Estate Association established a foundation for broader provincial concern about water-related climate matters when he reminded the audience that quality of life was a theme or lens through which his association defined its future. That Laing and his association not only supported but were attending the Not Waiting for Noah conference demonstrated how concern over the impacts of extreme weather events had begun to penetrate the fabric of the way of life of all British Columbians. Other presenters in the seminar made it clear, however, that despite its recent awakening to these issues, the province was still very much behind many places in the rest of the world in addressing the problem. This, it was pointed out, was in part a consequence of a generation lost to dithering and paying undue attention to climate change deniers.

The seminar also made clear that British Columbia was not starting at the beginning in terms of managing flood hazards. The provincial government was still simply reacting to flood issues, when what was needed was the re-engineering of landscapes and the restoration of ecosystems to reduce risk. The lower mainland, however, is awakening to the growing flood threat after being lulled into a false sense of safety by 60 years of dike improvements.

It was noted that flood recovery efforts do not include reduction of future flood losses. While some economic losses may be absorbed through these efforts, there is nothing in place that compensates for human suffering. Moreover, many flood hazard assessments in British Columbia are usually based on 20 year return events.

In a presentation entitled "We Are a Long Way from New Orleans," engineer and flood expert Tamsin Lyle reminded participants that assessments need to be done on risk, not just hazard, which requires analysis of potential chains of events. Manifold consequences need to be better characterized, including loss of life, destruction of property, contamination, economic loss, ecosystem impacts and loss of livestock and agricultural production.

Presentations at the "Not Waiting for Noah" seminar also underscored the importance of proactive land-use management as a means of floodproofing. Tools already exist that can be adapted to flood management purposes. The Insurance Bureau of Canada, for example, has developed a municipal risk assessment tool that can be used to quantify the risk of municipal storm sewage back-up under a variety of scenarios. The software can map the current and projected risk of system failure for any given municipality, neighbourhood by neighbourhood, over the coming century.

The proceedings of the seminar also made it clear that we need to be pressing for legislated flood assessments similar to those that came into existence in Europe in 2005. Risk is a moving target. Even 1 in 200 year return event standards may be irrelevant where there has been increased flood plain development. In his presentation on new engineering standards for British Columbia, Matthias Jakob urged planners to follow changes in hydro-climatic trends rather than relying on static 1 in 200 year flood numbers. Such statistics should now be seen as vestiges of that lost stationarity.

The proceedings of the seminar demonstrated that British Columbia was still very much at the mapping and planning stages of determining flood risks. There is yet little action in terms of proactive flood management. Multi-billion dollar flood protection projects are required if the lower mainland is to be protected from the threat of flooding from extreme weather events and from storm surges induced by sea level rise. New risk-based guidelines are being proposed that emphasize the need to plan for hydrological change in light of climate change and interconnected land-use changes. While these are presently only guidelines, it was noted that professional engineers and planners can be held legally liable if they don't follow them.

There is a fear that, as in the case of climate change, we have outstanding models to which, in policy terms, we pay little attention. If British Columbia wants to have effective flood protection, it has to invest seriously in it. If the province aimed for protection from much larger flood events, as other jurisdictions around the world have, the cost will be very high. Effective flood protection, however, is going to require this kind of investment, which in turn will require strong political support. For this reason, multi-stakeholder processes that don't include effective public outreach are unlikely to succeed. It is very important to bring together all the stakeholders in flood protection, not just engineers in different specialties.

Presently British Columbia is in a very vulnerable position. It is presently operating largely on 1 in 100 year and 1 in 200 year standards, which will not provide the kind of protection required in changing hydro-climatic conditions. Much of the province's present flood protection infrastructure is inadequate. Huge sums will be required to act on risks. Such risks, however, are increasing faster than we are moving to identify and address them, and until we can stabilize the climate, they will remain difficult to predict or to price. At present it appears that British Columbia faces at least a generation of growing vulnerability to serious flooding. What we have yet to see are tools that address the challenge of communicating this growing danger to the public. The conference did take note that there was urgency in moving on these matters, however. Why? As Hugh Fraser of the Corporation of Delta, BC, pointed out, "For every dollar you put into protection, you save five in damage."

All of this was very much on our minds when, on June 18, Environment Canada forecasted heavy rain in the Rockies.

The day before: Tuesday, June 18

It all started out innocently enough, as such things often do. It began to rain. It was June; no one was surprised. Few, however, had heeded the forecast. On Tuesday, June 18, the day before the flooding began upstream in the mountains, the *Calgary Herald* published a weather update predicting up to 150 millimetres of rain for areas west and northwest of the city. The report put Calgarians on notice that a low-pressure system was expected to bring heavy rain to western Alberta beginning Wednesday morning, with up to 100 millimetres expected by Thursday evening. Some areas, the report said, could see even heavier rainfalls. The article quoted Environment Canada meteorologist Bill McMurtry, who explained that an unstable air mass, combined with moisture and warmer temperatures, could also bring thunderstorms to the area. McMurtry encouraged Albertans to keep checking the weather forecast and keep an eye on the skies.

As it happened, hydrologist and climate scientist John Pomeroy and his 15-member research team from the University of Saskatchewan Centre for Hydrology happened to be in the Canmore and Kananaskis area throughout the flooding. As a result, we are fortunate to have minute-by-minute, hour-by-hour observations of the changes in hydrological circumstances in the region throughout the flood period.

Day 1 of the flood: Wednesday, June 19

According to the *Rocky Mountain Outlook*, the town of Canmore began observing the rising creek at 7:00 on the evening of Wednesday, June 19. Nearly five hours before that, Pomeroy had emailed a colleague, Kevin Shook in Saskatoon, an expert hydrological modeller, to say there had already been a lot of rain in the past week and that rivers were already high. He noted also that the spring snowmelt was late and that the snowpack was above normal for late June. Pomeroy told Shook that while the provincial agency responsible for flood prediction in Alberta had issued a high streamflow advisory, it had stopped short of issuing a flood watch.

In the context of what happened in the following days, definitions matter. In issuing a high streamflow advisory, Alberta Environment is warning that water levels in the area of concern are rising or expected to rise rapidly but that *no major flooding* is expected. Minor flooding in low-lying areas, however, is possible. The warning advises anyone situated close to the streams affected to be cautious. When Alberta Environment issues a flood watch it means that streams in a given area are rising and will approach or may overtop banks. Flooding of areas adjacent to these streams may occur, and anyone located nearby is advised to take appropriate precautions. The next level of advisory – a flood warning – makes it clear that rising flows in a given area *will* result in flooding adjacent to the streams affected and advises anyone there to take appropriate measures to avoid damage. Pomeroy referred Shook to the Alberta Environment flood forecast website, where he could see what was happening for himself. The last words of Pomeroy's email were: "I see a screw-up coming." It would take months and media appeals to freedom of information legislation for Albertans to discover just how true Pomeroy's off-hand remark really was.

Shook responded seven minutes later. He had checked the stream gauge data on the website and reported that the Bow River at Banff was flowing at about 145 cubic metres a second. "In Canmore," he said, "basements start flooding at 240 cubic metres a second and the Bow River will overtop its banks at about 495 cubic metres a second." He concluded his email by saying, "It'll be interesting."

The *Rocky Mountain Outlook* reported that at 9:00 p.m. on Wednesday, June 19, Canmore Fire and Rescue was called to Cougar Creek to monitor stream levels. By 11:30 the creek had reached the top of the culverts at Bow Valley Trail and the Canadian Pacific Railway was already trying to prevent their tracks from washing out. As it happened, another of Pomeroy's research colleagues was there to observe first-hand what was happening. He reported that CP Rail was "trying to save the railroad bridge from impending doom with three massive backhoes dredging the creek." The railway culvert was submerged and water was only half a metre from going over the top. The tracks, he said, "may not last the night, as an unbelievable volume of water is moving down the channel." Finally, the researcher referred to an attached audio recording and closed with: "Thought you'd appreciate hearing the boulders grinding down the bed of Cougar Creek."

Half an hour later, at just after midnight, John Pomeroy drove down to see for himself how Cougar Creek was doing. The road, he reported, was closed off, with water overtop. He confirmed that crews were working to dredge the creek as his researcher had reported. Pomeroy also reported that the police were there and prepared to arrest anyone coming closer, so he could not see the railway bridge. He noted, however, that the upper creek by the Iron Goat Restaurant was full and blasting away at its banks and that water had already backed up into streets and homes in the Spring Creek area. Pomeroy further pointed out that what he was seeing was way too close to what he had predicted to a journalist who quoted him in an article in the *Calgary Herald* nearly a month before.

The May 26 article, by Matt McClure, was headlined "Alberta urged to prepare for increasingly severe weather as insurance losses mount." The story cited a new report prepared by the Insurance Bureau of Canada for the Institute for Catastrophic Loss Reduction which predicted that Alberta would see a 10 per cent increase in severe weather events as average annual temperatures rise by as much as 4°C between now and 2050. Citing a sixfold increase in insured damages from severe storms, wildfire and flooding, the Insurance Bureau argued that the province and its municipalities needed to get serious about mitigating losses in Alberta, which had mounted to an average of $670-million in each of the past four years, compared to an average of $100-million annually for the previous 15 years. The article also cited polling conducted for the Insurance Bureau which found that 91 per cent of Canadians had noticed changes in weather patterns over the past decade. The fact that only 80 per cent of Albertans had noticed the same trends showed that residents of the province were less likely than other Canadians to be concerned over weather pattern changes that have made Albertans the worst hit in the country in terms of natural catastrophes.

The "new normal" in climatic conditions, the report noted, will result in more intense rainstorms that could cause flash flooding in low-lying areas that will overwhelm existing storm sewer systems. In response to that observation, Pomeroy had indicated that big frontal weather systems are already increasing in intensity and frequency and that "we are fast learning that our roads, bridges and even some of our towns aren't any match for the rainfall and the overflow that results." He then pointed directly to the flood threat in Canmore. "While Alberta's infrastructure is better able to withstand the threat of increased flooding than that in other western provinces," he said, "there are areas like the Cougar Creek subdivision in Canmore that are especially vulnerable." On this matter, it brought John Pomeroy no satisfaction to have been right. "Poor Canmore," he lamented in his email. "Be very careful tomorrow," he warned his colleagues, "and if you live in the valley bottom, be watchful tonight."

Day 2: Thursday, June 20

Less than half an hour after Pomeroy told his colleagues what he had seen, Cougar Creek breached the Trans-Canada Highway and Bow Valley Trail in Canmore. At 1:54 a.m. the RCMP detachment in Canmore advised that the Trans-Canada would be closed in both directions. Bow Valley Trail in Canmore and Highway 1A between Canmore and Exshaw would be closed as well. At the same time, a mudslide resulted in the closure of Highway 40 in Kananaskis. A second mudslide caused closure of the Trans-Canada within two kilometres of the Norquay overpass in Banff National Park. Within a few minutes of these road closures, the Town of Canmore, RCMP and volunteer members of Pomeroy's research team began knocking on doors in the Cougar Creek subdivision to warn residents to be prepared to evacuate.

At 2:45 a.m. Alberta Environment issued a flood watch for the Highwood River and its tributaries and the Sheep River but not for the Elbow or the Bow and their tributaries upstream. Fifteen minutes later, at 3:00, the Town of Canmore established an emergency operations centre. Forty-five minutes later a local state of emergency was declared in the communities of Canmore, Lac des Arcs and Exshaw.

At 3:59, May Guan, one of John Pomeroy's research colleagues, emailed to report she had just returned from several hours as a volunteer knocking on doors in the Cougar Creek area to warn residents of the pending evacuation. She reported that some of the homes closest to the most eroded banks were already being evacuated. Guan noted there was a *lot* of bank erosion. She also observed that the railway tracks and Highway 1A were ruined and that water and trees were flowing over the Trans-Canada. Transport trucks were parked off the highway west of the creek but some traffic was also being diverted around the flooding by way of the Three Sisters Parkway. Just as Guan was sending her email, the RCMP began mandatory evacuation of residents south of the nearly submerged pedestrian bridge on Cougar Creek.

The rain and flooding continued throughout the night, however. At 5:50 that morning, Alberta Environment issued another flood watch update, reporting that since Wednesday morning an intense low-pressure system had brought 60 to 90 millimetres of precipitation and in some places up to 150 millimetres in the mountains and along the foothills from Edson to Waterton National Park. It noted that this weather system was forecast to bring total rainfall of between 100 and 150 millimetres by Friday. This update elevated the Elbow River upstream of the Glenmore dam to flood watch status, but despite already massive flooding in Canmore and Exshaw, Alberta Environment maintained only a high streamflow advisory for the Bow and its upstream tributaries. (For the complete record of Alberta Environment advisories see www.environment.alberta.ca/forecasting/advisories/archives0613.html.)

By 6:15 a.m. the power was out in many parts of Canmore, and the road connecting Benchlands Trail and Eagle Terrace subdivision had been destroyed. The Trans-Canada and Highway 40 in Kananaskis were closed, as well as the Three Sisters Parkway. Pomeroy ordered his research team to stay home as long as it was safe and to let the emergency crews do their jobs. He also instructed them to check the Town of Canmore website for detailed updates. Just as Dr. Pomeroy pressed "send" to dispatch his email, an evacuation centre was established at Elevation Place, the town's recently completed recreation complex. A half-hour later 23 truckers and an RCMP officer became trapped by floodwaters on the Trans-Canada Highway and had to be rescued by helicopter.

At 8:45, almost six hours after a state of emergency had already been declared in Canmore, Alberta Environment issued an official flood warning update that upgraded the main stem of the Bow River upstream and downstream of Calgary and the Elbow River downstream of Glenmore dam from a high streamflow advisory to a flood watch. The Highwood and its tributaries, the Elbow upstream of Glenmore dam and the tributaries of the Bow upstream of Calgary, including Cougar Creek, were upgraded from flood watch to flood warning.

At 9:46 Pomeroy emailed graduate students who were at the Biogeoscience Institute at Barrier Lake Field Station in Kananaskis to warn them to watch out for debris flows through the station grounds.

At 12:36 p.m. one of Dr. Pomeroy's post-doctoral research fellows reported that the culverts on the major roads and railways in the Canmore area were already overwhelmed, dramatically impacting development on the flood plain. "I am watching right now," he said, "as the Canmore hospital becomes an island as a result of the runoff from the benchlands above flowing over the Trans-Canada." Alberta's flood plain map, he pointed out, indicated that the area should be high and dry.

An hour later, Kevin Shook commented from Saskatoon that the flood event that was taking place highlighted at least seven weaknesses in the province's flood warning system.

First of all, Shook explained, the Alberta Environment flood map only shows what would be estimated for a 1 in 100 year event. There was presently no way of knowing how big the present flood might be.

The flood map was also inaccurate in part because Cougar Creek and the other tributary streams in the affected area were in ungauged basins, meaning there were no streamflow or other instruments in the creek that would help improve the accuracy of flood forecasts. Also evident to Shook was that the flow estimates in Alberta Environment's flood model had been done with very crude tools, which suggested to him that the model had probably been developed in the 1980s or 1990s.

He further noted that hydraulic models used for flood plain mapping don't account for erosion, of which much was occurring in Cougar Creek and other tributaries flowing into the Bow in the area encompassed by the storm.

As the degree of uncertainty in projected flow estimates was not quantified, Shook pointed out, anyone looking at the Alberta Environment model would think that such estimates were hard, reliable numbers, when that was clearly not the case.

Finally, he noted, there was the human factor. "Cities and towns," he said, "have the incentive to sell as much land as possible, but they don't get the bill when there is flood damage." Shook was referring to inappropriate development in floodplains for which the provincial and federal governments – and not municipalities – become responsible in the event of major overland flooding.

At 4:00 p.m. the residents of Lac des Arcs were evacuated with the assistance of the Cochrane fire department. At 4:01 researcher Keith Musselman emailed the team to report that radar was right then tracking what could be the heaviest rain of the event moving into the Bow Valley. He noted that storm cells east and south of Morley were moving in the direction of Canmore. He warned his colleagues not to be fooled by any lull in precipitation they may be experiencing. Waters will continue to rise very quickly if this trend persists, he said. "Please be careful if you are out."

Day 3: Friday, June 21

During the night, a spectacularly swollen pulse of floodwater flowed downstream from the mountains into the unprepared city of Calgary. Twenty neighbourhoods were evacuated, with more than 100,000 people forced from their homes. But Calgary wasn't the only municipality that was in trouble. Twelve southern Alberta communities had declared states of emergency, and eight besides Calgary were under evacuation orders.

The flooding was particularly serious in small towns immediately south of Calgary. High River, Turner Valley and Black Diamond were all affected by the floodwaters of the Highwood River, which swept away three people. The river had risen so quickly at High River that residents became trapped in their cars and homes and had to be rescued from their roofs. Streets literally became rivers, swamping vehicles. Even rescue boats had trouble with the strong currents while trying to navigate along downtown streets. High River was almost completely obliterated. Two-thirds of the community was flooded and 5,000 residents were forced from their homes, including the author's sister and her husband, who lost everything. Seven months later my sister died, her already frail health having failed partly because of the stress she endured as a result of the flooding.

The flooding attracted immediate political attention, certainly in Alberta but also elsewhere in Canada. At 9:36 a.m. the premier's office in Edmonton announced that Alison Redford would personally tour Lethbridge, Canmore and High River later in the day.

At 10:40 Prime Minister Stephen Harper left Ottawa for Calgary to survey the damage. Aerial images of the city that morning showed extensive flooding in many neighbourhoods near the Bow and Elbow rivers but also significant flooding in the concentrated downtown area.

At 11:00, just after Prime Minister Harper's

plane took off, the City of Medicine Hat announced that an emergency operations centre had been established in response to what were predicted to be flows in the South Saskatchewan River in excess of 6000 cubic metres a second. A local state of emergency was announced a few hours later as the combined flows of the Bow and Oldman tributaries which form the South Saskatchewan began to rise rapidly to levels that were expected to exceed the record flood of 1995 by at least 600 cubic metres per second .

Later in the day, Calgary mayor Naheed Nenshi demonstrated the true grit of his city by announcing that despite the flood the Calgary Stampede would be held July 5–14 as scheduled, come hell or high water. At 3:00 p.m., however, the city asked residents to limit their water use to reduce demand on the drinking water treatment plants. While the City maintained that drinking water quality had not been compromised, it was clear that water infrastructure was under siege.

Meanwhile, back in the mountains, a flood warning issued for the towns of Banff and Canmore indicated that the Bow River had received 250 millimetres of precipitation since

Wednesday morning. John Pomeroy already knew this, long before the flood warning was issued. In an interview with *Calgary Herald* reporter Colette Derworiz, Pomeroy made it clear that what was happening in Canmore was his worst nightmare. Pomeroy also predicted that the flood could get worse before it got better. "The outlook is for more rain," he said, noting that additional precipitation would result in more runoff to produce even higher streamflows. He added that the weather system had not moved on and that the residents of the Bow valley should not let down their guard.

At 8:14 p.m. the Conservative Party of Alberta emailed a statement to card-carrying members in which Premier Redford expressed concern for the people and communities that had been impacted by the flood. The premier went on to explain that upon arriving in Calgary to view the flood damage first-hand she had met with Municipal Affairs Minister Doug Griffiths and Colin Lloyd, the managing director of the Alberta Emergency Management Agency. Because the power was out in much of Calgary, the premier reported standing on a bridge in the dark and listening to what she described as the terrifying roar of the Bow River.

The premier also reported in a regular news release to party members that after visiting Canmore she then returned to Calgary, where she and Prime Minister Harper surveyed the damage by helicopter. Ironically, Premier Redford concluded her official statement of June 21 with a promise to report to party members the following week on her recent successful trip to New York City to promote the Keystone XL pipeline. According to *The Globe and Mail*, Redford had "delivered an ardent pitch for expanded development of her province's oil sands, calling it critical to the long-term growth and security of the United States and Canada." Without even so much as a hint of irony, the last sentence in Premier Redford's official release urged party members to "pull together and help each other get through this crisis." It apparently did not occur to the premier that such remarks demonstrated that she and her government did not see any obvious link between growing greenhouse gas emissions and the growing intensity of extreme weather events that ultimately caused the very catastrophe she was commenting upon.

Day 4: Saturday, June 22

As the rains subsided the following day some 1,300 Canadian soldiers were sent into flood zones. An obviously shaken but very genuine Premier Redford announced a billion dollars in emergency disaster relief. But even as the media communicated the news to devastated flood victims it was clear the damage was likely an order of magnitude greater than the aid the premier was promising. As shock subsided into despair for so many, the blame game began. George Groeneveld, a former Alberta MLA who had headed up a flood mitigation task force after the 2005 event, went on record to say that new development should never have been allowed in the flood zones identified in his task force's report. Other old flood-risk reports full of ignored recommendations surfaced amidst shouting matches over who was responsible for what, who had failed in their responsibilities and who ought to be sued by developers and property owners as a result. Even the crazies entered the fray. One man charged that the flood was a message to the Bow Valley from God for the brutal extermination of feral rabbits at the hands of the mayor and council of Canmore.

Under fire with respect to the flooding, the Alberta government appeared more interested in managing the message than managing the actual mess. This proved to be the case also with political opponents such as the Wildrose party, who at first misjudged the importance of everyone in the province pulling together in the face of genuine disaster that brought about real tragedy for so many.

On October 4, 107 days after the devastating 2013 flood, Premier Alison Redford opened the official Alberta Flood Mitigation Symposium by stating that the 2013 disaster had fundamentally changed the definition of what it meant to be an Albertan.

Unfortunately, the symposium was not really a symposium at all. Clumsily as it appeared to be organized, it was first and foremost a carefully orchestrated public relations event meant to serve the political interests of the party in power. Little dialogue was encouraged, and when it was permitted it was constrained in a way that did not countenance penetrating questions or differing points of view. When questions served the interests of the organizers, they were answered – more or less;

but when questions ran contrary to the objectives set, they were dismissed or deferred. It was not discovered until nearly two months later that the reason why questions at the forum were so carefully controlled was that there was information concerning the predictability of the flood which the government of Alberta did not want to share.

No one present called the government on their obvious effort to control the message, however, and the issue of spin continues to be problematic in the flood debate in Alberta. Spin can be defined as a conscious attempt to shape the perceptions and actions of others around a vision of reality the governing party and their political allies have created to defend or advance specific interests. The risk is that over time – and by way of much repetition – those engaged in spin start believing the vision of reality they are attempting to create, and that is when the unseen whale that is the larger truth often invades.

The underlying political tone of the symposium was that the Alberta government had everything under control, that everything was on the way to being fixed. After years of cutbacks and lapses in attention and focus, suddenly the government was all over this issue, with a sincerity and intensity rarely displayed or imagined before. As is customary in Alberta, a government official announced once more that the province is about to be a world leader, this time in flood mitigation. Albertans are used to such proclamations. For the last decade we have pronounced ourselves world leaders in water management. Even though the flood rather questioned that assertion, we are now on to the next thing. We are going to declare ourselves world leaders in flood protection.

It should be noted, however, that the symposium was helpful in that it did deal specifically in practical ways to improve flood protection and mitigation. The government of Alberta announced that it was taking a systemic approach to addressing the province's flood mitigation needs based on three principles: collaboration and cooperation; partnerships and inclusiveness; and resilience as expressed by layers of readiness. These three principles were to be supported by seven nested components that support integrated flood management, including overall watershed management; the capacity to model and predict what is happening; the development of flood risk policies that acknowledge the need to assure the functional integrity of floodways; and the importance of appropriate water and flood management infrastructure and erosion control. The province also noted that local mitigation initiatives will be necessary at the municipal level, and that individual property owners will have to take more responsibility for protecting themselves. So, all politics and communications spin-doctoring aside, what did we learn in Alberta?

Alberta lessons learned

1. Our flood prediction systems are inadequate.

While the province did many things right after the flood, it was clear the right systems were not in place to predict and manage an event of this magnitude. Though the government refused to acknowledge this, the first problem was that the province's flood prediction system utterly failed.

In the final months of 2013, the emails noted in this book were subpoenaed under the Freedom of Information and Protection of Privacy Act and formed a large part of the content of a two-page *Calgary Herald* article by Matt McClure published on December 27. The article was the last of a progression of stories that in effect demolished many of the government's publicly stated positions with respect to the failure of their flood protection system.

Many were those who claimed that flooding of

the magnitude that occurred in southern Alberta could never have been anticipated. In the immediate wake of the disaster officials also argued that the flood was of such scope and occurred so quickly that nothing could have been done to prevent the damage and loss of life that occurred. Both claims are simply untrue. Flooding of this scope in Calgary had been predicted as early as 1979 and very nearly occurred in 2005. But that did not stop some politicians and others from claiming the 2013 flood was a once in a thousand years event. It wasn't. Calculations released by John Pomeroy and his team in late November 2013 indicate that this flood was a once in 45 year event in Calgary. As Pomeroy pointed out, it was not extraordinary; it was not the flood of the century; it was not even the flood of a lifetime. We just weren't prepared for it.

When, two months after the flood, the Minister of Environment, the Honourable Diana McQueen, argued that "no report or recommendations looking at the issues of the past could have prepared us for this event," she was wrong. In addition to other, previous studies, an analysis of the flood potential of the Bow and Elbow rivers had been initiated by Golder and Associates in 2009 and completed in 2012, a year before the flood. The Golder report showed that urban development in the floodway in Calgary from 1983 to the present increased the potential flood levels substantially because the development had reduced the room available for water to move and had slowed the floodwaters down, forcing them higher. The report predicted that if a major inundation were to hit Calgary it could cause unprecedented damage. Since the study had been commissioned by the provincial government in partnership with the City of Calgary, it would appear inconceivable that the minister responsible would not have known about it.

According to McClure and the *Herald*, officials had also been wrong about the state and readiness of the government's own flood prediction system. At the symposium presided over by the premier in Calgary on October 4, Alberta officials maintained that the government's flood prediction group had been in full readiness and had done everything in its power to properly inform communities that were under threat. Self-congratulatory officials at the symposium stated that flood prediction staff had slept in sleeping bags while dutifully carrying out their tasks during the flood. While that may have been true for a couple of forecasters, it turns out that key field technology staff who could have contributed in important ways to an accurate prediction were away at an ill-timed conference, where they were trapped for two days by the very floodwaters they failed to predict. It appears the reality is that Alberta Environment forecasters relied on models instead of observations; distrusted and then bet against their own data; and completely botched the prediction, thereby compounding the flood damage and putting the lives of hundreds of thousands of people at risk. In many places, flood warnings were not issued until hours after emergency evacuations were ordered. Flood volumes were three times what were initially predicted. Three people lost their lives.

As John Pomeroy pointed out in McClure's December 27 *Herald* article, Alberta's response to this flood "was reminiscent of what you would expect in a developing country." The government of Alberta kept weaknesses in its prediction system quiet for six months following the flood, a fact that seriously questions the government's commitment to transparency before, during and after the most expensive disaster in the history of the province. We might still not know the real facts relating to our utter failure to anticipate and predict the 2013 flood – or ever know them – had Matt McClure and the *Herald* not pressed for access to government emails through freedom of information legislation.

Together these revelations underscore a troubling point that continues to be glossed over at the time of this writing eight months later. Not only was there mismanagement and a complete lack of situational awareness within the responsible government department, but a good deal of evidence points to a cover-up at the highest political levels of what actually happened. National and international examples suggest that this is a dangerous path to take after a major disaster. After a flood event caused $700-million in damage and affected thousands of homes in Toronto in 2005, the head of Toronto Infrastructure observed that one of the biggest problems the city had to face in the ensuing years was to regain the confidence of the public. Officials in the government of Manitoba expressed similar sensitivities regarding public confidence after major flooding there in 2011. In Alberta the mayor of High River declared in the McClure article that the town would take its own readings and make its own flood predictions from now on. Later the Town of Canmore declared a similar interest. Critical liability issues aside, taking a do-it-yourself approach to flood prediction and warning is utterly misguided. Instead of working to improve the larger system as others elsewhere have done after serious floods, there has been a dangerous movement backwards toward atomization of prediction capacity, accountability and liability.

What happened in Alberta in June 2013 was interesting but hardly unpredictable. We need to learn from what went wrong. Clearly, it is time to move toward coupled hydrological and meteorological modelling in nearly real time. Enhanced modelling should ideally be linked to a denser network of mountain meteorological stations and stream gauge stations, especially in small tributary creeks prone to flash floods. What we really need, however, is a national flood prediction program of the kind that exists in the United States and in Europe, with stronger links and enhanced monitoring by the Water Survey of Canada to provincial programs. John Pomeroy was emphatic on this in a later newspaper interview: "We're about the only developed country in the world that doesn't have a unified flood prediction service," he said. "It is time we joined the rest of the developed world and started to save billions in flood damages by developing a first-class national strategy."

2. Our flood maps are outdated and irrelevant.

The second lesson we learned was that many of our provincial flood maps are inaccurate and largely irrelevant. While the City of Calgary's mapping proved correct, most of the province's 1994 flood maps are long out of date. They do not account for 20 years of urban development, landform changes, creek discharge or groundwater dynamics, nor for erosion and resulting debris torrents, nor for climate change or loss of stationarity. Neither do the province's maps take into account the fact that the value of vulnerable properties in flood plains in southern Alberta has increased exponentially since those maps were drawn. The outdated maps do not recognize that because of the broader societal value of what it is supposed to guard, flood protection today is worth orders of magnitude more than in the past and far, far more than it was worth, say, 50 years ago.

Using 20-year-old flood maps is rather like having a life crisis at age 50 and going back to your 30s and basing future choices on what you knew and what was happening then. Though we cling in Alberta to the current 1 in 100 year flood event standard, it tells us little. Alberta's flood maps are based on the estimated peak discharge, with a 1 per cent chance of occurring in any year. It tells us what might have been expected in 1950, when what we need to know is what to expect in 2050.

A consultant who presented at the Flood Mitigation Symposium used the following analogy to describe the problem with using such flow averages as the foundation for flood mapping. Almost all of us are air travellers, he began. Would you design a passenger airplane based on the average conditions in which it will be flown? No, you would design the plane to withstand known extremes and then add a margin of safety on top of that. That's how flood maps have to work.

Hydrologists need to do comparisons that focus on extremes in the same way that climate scientists compare a broad range of model outcomes to establish future scenarios.

3. Adapting to the new normal is going to be expensive.

Alberta also learned the hard way that the growing threat of extreme weather events demands that we are going to have to replace vulnerable infrastructure across the entire country with new systems designed to handle greater extremes.

In addition, Alberta learned – as others have – that the loss of hydrological stability has the potential to cause a great deal of human misery and suffering, even in a prosperous place. Disaster relief is not the same as insurance. Those on – or driven to – the margins will suffer the most, and if they are forgotten, their problems – as we have seen in Manitoba – will have legal and political consequences for governments at all levels for decades to come.

4. You can't go home again.

You can't un-know what you already know. There is always a temptation – and often a great deal of political pressure applied – after a disaster to try to remake the world as it was. But that will not be possible. We now have thousands of new data points that can tell us where the real flood plains are in southern Alberta. That is where we have to start.

5. Governments can't solve problems of this scale on their own.

You can't count on just the government to deal with this problem. Individuals have to take responsibility also. Everyone has to be involved in dealing with the increased threat of such events, and the problem will not be fully addressed unless that happens. Measures can and must be taken by individuals to better protect their families, their property and their communities from more frequent and intense weather events. The US has made disaster resilience a national imperative. We need to do that in Canada too.

There are, however, larger, overarching lessons we might learn from what we know about our changing hydro-climatic circumstances.

Overarching lessons learned

1. We need to begin controlling the hydrological cycle regionally and globally.

Hydrological regimes are constantly changing. We have been fortunate as a society, however, to have enjoyed relative hydrological stability during the recent period of huge population growth and infrastructure development. The lesson to be learned from such good fortune is that the loss of relative hydrological stability is a much bigger problem than we initially thought. The systemic threats we face are part of a single, connected hydrological whole. Every part of the water cycle flows through and affects and is affected by every other part. Changes in the extent and duration of Arctic sea ice and northern snowpack and continental snowcover have begun to have a cascading effect on weather and climate right down to the mid-latitudes.

The loss of relative hydrological stationarity is a societal game changer. It means that simply managing water in ways that are useful to us will no longer be enough. We now have to be alert to changes in the larger global hydrological cycle and, where possible, try to manage and adapt to them. This is a huge new concept and it is going to take time to get our heads around it.

2. What we have seen is what we are going to get.

Predicted rises in temperatures of between 2 and 6°C will result in increases 15 to 40 per cent or more in the capacity of the atmosphere to hold water vapour. This problem will not be going away. It certainly didn't go away after the flood waters receded in Alberta.

In the second part of this book Kerry Freek describes the flooding that took place in downtown Toronto only three weeks after the flooding in southern Alberta. Freek argues that the uncertainty of a changing climate clearly demands a faster response in Canada's major cities. She points out that making decisions and funding action in a municipality the size of Toronto is akin to moving mountains. The crippling costs of replacing an outdated stormwater system, Freek notes, combined with a host of competing political interests, are presently making it impossible for Toronto to become a resilient city.

The key lesson we learn from the 2013 flooding in Alberta and Ontario is that we are not prepared to deal with the climate variability and flood risk that exist now, let alone what we can expect as a more energetic atmosphere is able to transport more water vapour. These serious floods were nothing compared to what the atmosphere is capable of delivering now and in the future. This was made evident by a series of extreme weather events that occurred in Russia shortly afterward.

What happened in Russia is almost beyond imagination. It is almost the stuff of science fiction. The weakening of the European jet stream caused by reduced snow and sea ice cover led to the creation of a heat dome in northern Siberia. In July 2013 hundreds of wildfires broke out that were so hot they melted the permafrost beneath the burning forests, creating methane releases from the thawing tundra that added fuel to the fires. Then, in early August, in the midst of what was coming to resemble a virtual firestorm, three atmospheric rivers collided over the region and within four days created a flood that covered a million square kilometres. Again we see floods and fires of a magnitude seldom experienced before in the same basin in the same year. But we also see something much darker. It appears we are melting the frozen lid of the jar that contains much of the world's methane. Compared to this, opening Pandora's box is like unwrapping a Christmas present.

We then saw the same theme repeated right before our eyes in Colorado: fires and massive floods in the same basin in the same year. Colorado experts explained that the storm started when "a strong plume of tropical moisture moved up from Mexico." At first the rain was welcomed. It ended a severe drought and put out the forest fires. But then the storm simply parked itself over the state. Some 19.8 inches of rain fell in the Boulder area, which was unprecedented for the month of September. This is interesting but there was more. The state climatologist of Colorado, Nolan Doeskan, noted that the most remarkable feature of the storm was not the cloudburst per se but the atmospheric water levels. The storm, he said, "shattered all records for the most water vapour in the atmosphere." What we are experiencing now in terms of extreme weather events appears to be within the realm of natural variability we have experienced in the past. The storms of the future will almost certainly be of magnitudes that are outside that realm.

3. We can't do this ourselves; we need nature to help us.

While technological breakthroughs will be helpful, we can't rely on engineering alone. The metabolism of the world economy is fundamentally out of sync with that of natural process. Reconciliation with nature has to be at the centre of the adaptation agenda. In order to prevent further acceleration of the hydrological cycle, we have to enlist all the help nature can give us. We obtain that help by protecting and restoring natural storage and critical aquatic ecosystem function and by reversing land and soil degradation wherever we can.

4. Managing water on a basin scale is no longer merely optional.

In this context the watershed or catchment basin is the minimum unit at which water must managed. If we want to manage larger hydrological forces, we have little choice but to overcome jurisdictional fragmentation and institutional territoriality to make basin-scale water management a meaningful reality.

5. Sooner or later we have to address the root cause.

An urgent new societal priority is emerging. In order to protect our prosperity and assure societal stability, we need to do what is necessary to preserve the hydrological cycle as we know it. This means that sooner or later we may have to accept that climate change effects on water may cost our society more than our economy generates by ignoring those effects. Only then we will be able to adapt.

The new normal – regrettably – is that there is no new normal and won't be until we stabilize atmospheric temperatures. The initial goal of the Kyoto Protocol was to reduce global greenhouse emissions by 5 per cent compared to 1990 levels. Global carbon emissions are expected to reach a record 36 billion tons in 2013, which means that emissions from the burning of fossil fuels are now 61 per cent above 1990 levels. It is very difficult to adapt if you don't know what you have to adapt to. Unless we want our future to continue to be a moving target, sooner or later we may have to confront the root cause – climate change – which unfortunately remains a subject few want to talk about in meaningful terms, at least where I live in Alberta.

Creating and sustaining hope

So where do we go now? First, it is important to realize that no matter where we live in the world we are likely to face a much more variable global climate. A storm warning regarding hydro-climatic change is justified and all of us should pay attention to that. It won't be long before the storm is upon us. We need to prepare now.

Secondly, it is important to recognize that this is not the time to throw up our hands and declare the problem simply too complicated to address. Such behaviour is, in fact, irresponsible. The sky is not falling and the world is not coming to an end. While it is a complex problem, we have the means to manage hydro-climatic change. The problems we face, however, are indeed substantial. For that reason, if there was ever a time in history that demanded thoughtful and persistent leadership and inspired citizenship, it is now.

Finally, there is also the not insignificant matter of hope. As a witness to the rapid hydro-climatic destabilization that is taking place in Canada and abroad, I have often been asked if it is possible to have hope for the future. When I ask exactly what these people mean by hope the answer I most often receive relates to whether there is any hope for resolution of these problems before they accelerate beyond our capacity to manage them. Can we turn these problems around while they are still more or less linear and incremental, before they become non-linear and everything we rely on for stability in the world begins to change all at once. Others ask if there is any hope for their children or for the as yet unborn, which is to say inter-generational hope. The question then becomes whether we really do have the right to inflict irreparable damage on all subsequent generations.

Hope will be a critical element in adaptation. Without it we are not likely to act effectively enough quickly enough to make a difference to our future. Much current hopelessness emerges out of the recognition that our political systems are not designed and structured in such a manner that would easily allow them to be capable of addressing issues of this magnitude. Their time and space scales are all wrong. While political systems are designed to function within limited, and often competing, jurisdictions over timeframes of only a few years, the climate problems we have created for ourselves are multigenerational and global in extent. Many don't believe it is possible to rescue our political systems from the influence of vested economic and ideological interests and the self-referential focus of party politics, in time to prevent collapse of important elements of the Earth system. Where this view predominates, many stop even trying to reframe the problem in any personally meaningful way. The problem is just too big to solve. Despair emerges out of a perceived helpless to do anything to prevent the society we are part of from sliding over the edge into the abyss.

Thus we find ourselves back at the turning point where we started, before the flood. If changing hydro-climatic conditions persist – and they are expected to do so – Albertans will look to their politicians and experts for accurate information, direction, leadership and ultimately hope. If all they can expect from our leaders and their elites is short-sighted self-interest and self-serving public-relations manipulation of facts and issues, then helplessness and despair will ultimately rule the day. People will continue to die prematurely and valuable property will continue to be needlessly destroyed.

While it is important to recover from the flood – and to ensure that no one is left behind due to its impacts – it is equally important to understand what really happened and what should happen next so that we can prepare now for the future. The hope is that the flood taught us all something, and that perhaps our politicians will see that we owe it to those who have suffered so much to make Calgary and region the place where Alberta started to get it right for next time. For *there will be* a next time. And a time after that.

PART TWO: TORONTO

What need the bridge much broader than the flood?
— DON PEDRO in *Much Ado About Nothing*,
1.1.288

There is no such thing as a 100-year flood.
— ANDREW CUOMO, Governor of New York,
on Hurricane Sandy

Being followed by the water

In June 2013, Toronto and the rest of Canada watched as a storm submerged much of southern Alberta, causing untold hardship for people in High River, Calgary and nearby towns.

Just a few days after the initial flooding – the rivers still swollen and the downtown covered in puddles – I watched the news from my hotel room at the Calgary airport, my eyes glued to mayor Naheed Nenshi as he addressed the city throughout the emergency, providing hourly updates and warnings.

I was in town for the unexpectedly well-timed Canadian Water Summit, relocated, within hours of the rainfall, from the flooded Saddledome arena to the airport hotel. The event gave Alberta's water experts a forum to speak with their peers between long shifts of helping their family, friends and colleagues salvage their homes. A rapid-fire breakfast session captured some of their observations and outrage. Their warnings had gone unheard and Albertans were once again about to pay the price of inaction. Indeed, the Insurance Bureau of Canada eventually reported billions of dollars of damage to infrastructure, buildings and homes.

Back home, Torontonians nervously joked about how our city would handle such an emergency. If similarly fierce rains happened here, could we weather the storm?

We should have knocked on wood. Not more than three weeks later, the skies above Toronto opened and, with very little warning, dumped some 100 millimetres of rain in just two hours, exceeding the previous record for same-day rainfall, set on October 15, 1954. The July 8 storm overwhelmed portions of the city's sewer system, sending more than a million cubic metres of raw sewage into streets, parks, Lake Ontario and the Don River. It left 37 of 69 city transit stations without service, trapped 1,400 passengers (and, famously, one snake) on a commuter train for three hours, left 300,000 residents without power, caused major flight delays at both the city and international airports and flooded unknown numbers of basements.

Leaving work that night, I abandoned any hope of public transit (streetcars were stalled in the middle of the streets), fashioned a makeshift raincoat from a garbage bag and began my journey home on foot. Darting between raindrops on King Street in the downtown centre of Old Toronto, I watched with amazement as a manhole became a geyser, shooting raw sewage into the air like a sloppy Jet d'eau de Genève. It was indeed a marvel, but hardly a triumphant celebration of city life.

I was one of the lucky ones. In the following months, Torontonians would learn the storm set a record for Ontario insured damages arising from a single natural disaster, triggering more than $940-million in private claims, according to the Insurance Bureau of Canada. Other estimates revealed the storm would cost the City of Toronto more than $60-million in repairs, a mere $5-million of which was covered by insurance.

Canadians are becoming increasingly aware that climate change is no longer some abstract idea. And, according to the Intergovernmental Panel on Climate Change, Ontario can expect more frequent thunderstorms in the coming years. For an older city like Toronto, extreme wet weather is a growing risk and a serious challenge. But if you remove climate change from the equation (I've left most of the hydro-climatic science to my co-author), the city would still have a big problem.

Here's what I know. Flooding is part of a natural cycle. Healthy crops grow on fertile land when floods spread nutrients across fields. In times of drought, a flood can help recharge watercourses and aquifers. But when we build cities and homes – what photographer Edward Burtynsky calls "human systems" – near water, we interrupt this natural flow. Pavement acts as a barrier or seal, forcing water to find new places to go, with the result that we put ourselves and our environment (both built and natural) at risk. And when Toronto flooded on July 8, we came face to face with our flawed urban composition. We have pretended we don't have to follow the rules.

The uncertainty of a changing climate demands a faster response, but making decisions and funding action in a municipality like Toronto can be akin to moving mountains. An unfit stormwater system, the crippling cost of replacing it, a host of competing political interests and a largely oblivious public prevent Toronto from becoming a resilient city. Unless we're willing to accept further and more extensive damage, it's time to make a big shift. We must define what we value and measure our actions accordingly. Is Toronto up to the challenge?

Hazel's legacy (in brief)

Despite the extensive damage to personal and public property this past summer, experts believe we've come a long way – that is to say, the July 8 storm could have had a much worse impact.

Sixty years ago, Toronto and much of southern Ontario experienced a storm of unprecedented strength. From October 15 to 18, 1954, Hurricane Hazel ravaged two watersheds, flooded several watercourses and drowned many towns. Eighty-one people died, 1,868 families were left homeless and damages were estimated to be $25-million ($217.6-million in 2013 dollars).

John Kinkead, director of water resources management and restoration at Credit Valley Conservation, says Toronto and area suffered so much damage because nobody fathomed the size of the event. "We're much better prepared now due to things like floodplain regulations," he says.

"Though we dodged a bullet with Hurricane Sandy last summer, it could have been a reenactment of Hazel."

Eight years before Hazel, the province had passed the Conservation Authorities Act in response to agricultural, naturalist and sportsmen's groups' concerns about the impacts of poorly managed land, water and forests, including erosion and drought. The Act gave regional conservation authorities the power to study their watersheds and determine programs to conserve, restore, develop and manage natural resources and control waters to prevent floods or pollution.

But the 1954 hurricane taught Toronto some hard lessons and revealed a growing need for even better management. Ultimately, Hazel's rampage prompted significant amendments to the Act in 1956, notably to empower conservation authorities to make regulations to prohibit filling in floodplains. Over the ensuing years, the government further focused these regulations. Conservation authorities now had a say regarding any dumping of fill in areas that may affect flood control, pollution or conservation. As of 1968 they could also prohibit or control construction and alterations to waterways. Revisions in 1998 expanded those powers to include regulation of development and interference with wetlands and alterations to shorelines and watercourses.

To properly manage these areas, conservation authorities needed a way to define and measure a floodplain. Since conditions vary from region to region, the Regulatory Flood Plain became the approved standard in Ontario, and it is set based on an epic "regional storm," the 100-year flood or a recorded storm of note for the region. Within the jurisdiction of the Toronto and Region Conservation Authority (TRCA) and much of the nearby area, the Regulatory Flood Plain is based on a storm of Hurricane Hazel's proportions.

To do something about costs associated with rising disaster assistance claims, the federal government in 1975 launched the Flood Damage Reduction Program (FDRP) under the Canada Water Act to discourage further development in vulnerable areas. In cooperation with the provinces, some 900 communities were mapped based on the 100-year storm (or more stringent provincial definitions). Taking part in the program meant both parties agreed not to build or support any future development in vulnerable zones.

At that time, Toronto was already quite far along in flood protection planning and execution. In 1959 the TRCA had released a three-stage plan that called for 15 control dams (five were eventually built), identified four major flood control channels (12 now exist, plus two major dikes) and resulted in more than 280 erosion control works. In 1960 the conservation authority began acquiring land in floodplains to transfer liability from private owners and make room for flood controls. The second stage involved construction of dams, reservoirs and other works. And in the third stage, the TRCA implemented new provincial regulations to restrict future development and land use in risky areas. Today the land acquired is part of a parks system that provides green space along watercourses that Torontonians and wildlife can enjoy.

And so it was Hurricane Hazel – the storm nobody expected – that transformed flood management in Ontario. Today there are 36 conservation authorities managing flood protection in watersheds that are home to 90 per cent of Ontario's population. But despite legislation, regulations and best-laid plans, recent events prove Toronto isn't immune to significant impacts of extreme weather. A 2005 storm triggered $671-million in claims, and a sequel in 2009 racked up $228-million. After the lessons of Hazel and progressive moves to better manage floodplains, why is the city still vulnerable to such costly damage?

There are a few things to consider here. First, the floodplain mapping completed during the 1970s FDRP did not account for increasingly extreme weather. It's true that Toronto didn't suffer on July 8 the same way it did back in 1954, but Hazel's intensity and volume per hour was nothing compared to the 2013 storm. Secondly, while the conservation authorities have done a commendable job managing floodplains, a city of concrete surfaces presents a major obstacle to watershed-scale protection. The July 8 storm overwhelmed sewers as well as watercourses. Urban flooding certainly does not preclude flooded riverbanks, but it is a different kind of event. While the TRCA does run a comprehensive stormwater management program, it is all those who make decisions about city design, from the municipal planner right down to individual homeowners, who are responsible for the consequences of their choices.

To this day, urban flooding is not a provincially recognized emergency in Ontario – a sore point for some – and the responsibility for its management falls to municipalities and their bylaws. Since Hazel, a combination of political will, city growth and increasingly extreme weather has changed the playing field. Using the context of Toronto's July 8 flood, the following pages discuss the challenges and provide some food for thought for moving forward.

An under-designed city

What have we learned about cities since Hazel? As John Kinkead simply states, flooding is not restricted to floodplains. Ontario has spent lots of time and money regulating floodplains to reduce the risk posed by swollen watercourses, but Toronto floods in spite of these efforts. It has to do with how we've designed the city and managed its growth.

Another fact: Toronto's infrastructure is old. The media often report on the national infrastructure deficit – last estimated at $145-billion[1] – in the context of aging assets, but the age of a pipe doesn't necessarily mean it is at risk of failure. On the contrary, some pipes are truly built to last – the oldest ones in Toronto are older than Canada! But, in the face of a changing climate and a growing population, it's easy to spot an older urban system's weak points, particularly outdated building practices and insufficient capacity. Toronto's combined sewers, for instance, are a design of the past – nobody with today's knowledge would think to build a growing city using them.

Popular in early 20th-century urban design, combined sewers take stormwater from streets as well as wastewater from neighbourhoods to the treatment plant. They're designed to send any overflow directly to outfalls – the places where drains and sewers empty into waterways – during excessive rain events. Combined sewers serve 25 per cent of Toronto's population today.

The rest of the city's network is composed of sanitary and storm sewers. When the volume of sewage and rainfall exceeds the capacity of the network, operators choose to divert – or bypass – that volume, sending water to the nearest outfall with little or no treatment. This action prevents sewage from ending up in basements or streets, but it does little to protect the environment surrounding the outfall – namely, Lake Ontario. The water includes input from combined sewers, sanitary sewers and groundwater infiltration. Storm sewers send water to settling tanks for some level of treatment or directly to the lake. According to a 2013 Ecojustice report, typical municipal sewage is a "foul cocktail of biological and chemical pollutants, including human waste, micro-organisms, disease-causing pathogens such as viruses and bacteria, and hundreds of toxic chemicals and heavy metals."[2] When we have a heavy storm, we allow a version of that cocktail to pour into the Great Lakes.

After the July 8 storm, Torontonians were not readily offered information about bypass volumes, so the charitable organization Lake Ontario Waterkeeper – whose motto is "Swim, Drink, Fish" – submitted a freedom of information request to the City, asking for numbers associated with sewage bypasses on the day of the storm. Almost four months later the organization found that the Ashbridges Bay and the Humber wastewater treatment plants reported a bypass total of 1,072,210 m^3 for that day. That's virtually the same as filling just over 428 Olympic-sized swimming pools with a combination of rain and raw sewage. Granted, Toronto's plants have holding tanks that allow them to treat some of that water to some degree once the demand subsides, but conversely the bypass figures don't include combined-sewer overflows, because the city doesn't measure those. No wonder the Ecojustice report card gives Toronto an F for both bypasses and CSOs and rates the city tenth of 12 municipalities for these categories!

Civil engineer Abe Khademi says Toronto is under-designed, which he admits isn't a fair term. What he means is the city was designed based on the science and knowledge of the day. When Toronto's first extensive sewage system was built, in the 19th century, city planners were not likely imagining a service for millions of people. Over the decades, Toronto's sewer system has been expanded to meet the needs of the growing city, but during events like the one on July 8, it falls short – especially in older parts that have not yet been converted to a separated system. Much of the city's inherited sewer infrastructure does not have the capacity to handle a changing climate that threatens wildly increased precipitation.

Khademi says there's no real consensus on how to address the notion of climate change in urban design: "The traditional practice uses a statistical analysis based on previous years of rainfall data, but notions of climate change call into question the design basis for the things we're building now."

The paved urban streetscape is also to blame. During a storm, water needs a place to go. In a natural system (fields, streams, grass etc.), rain filters through the ground to aquifers or runs off into ponds, lakes, rivers or streams. When rain lands on pavement, it flows until it finds a place to infiltrate. There are a few problems with flow in the urban context. In 2008, impervious surfaces (driveways, sidewalks, parking lots etc.) covered 26.7 per cent of Toronto, while buildings accounted for 20.6 per cent.[3] Buildings and other obstructions divert stormwater from a natural path, and as it flows over these surfaces it collects things you'd expect to find on a city street, including toxins, salt and garbage. There's no way the city's built systems can capture and treat all stormwater, so there's no telling what might end up in Lake Ontario or the Don River, and when we develop land without accounting for stormwater flow, we exacerbate the issue.

Extreme flows can also cause major disruptions and emergencies. During the July 8 storm, flooded areas compromised major transportation and transit routes during rush hour. Many people were trapped on expressways and forced to abandon their vehicles; Twitter lit up with photos of people sloshing their way to safety. One Toronto lawyer had to say a sad goodbye to his $200,000 Ferrari when Lower Simcoe Street flooded.

Not only are Ontario municipalities forced to deal with a future of weather-related surprises, they are also being asked to accommodate larger populations. Under the provincial Places to Grow Act, the City of Toronto must plan for a minimum gross density target of 400 residents and jobs combined per hectare for each of its urban growth centres by 2031. The Greater Golden Horseshoe, of which Toronto is a part, is forecast to grow by an additional 3.7 million (from 2001) to 11.5 million people. That's more than 80 per cent of Ontario's population growth, and it will place significant strain on an already stressed system.[4]

So how do we offset growth and the impacts of climate change in an under-designed city? The simple answer would be to "slow the flow" – that is, provide some relief to existing drainage systems by slowing or reducing the flow of stormwater to the system. Toronto has done a lot of work on that goal to date, but it's not as easy as it seems.

City design must be adaptive

Dealing with insufficient infrastructure in a concrete jungle seems like a major challenge – and it is. Khademi says separating combined sewers is an obvious step, but it's a massive, expensive undertaking and certainly not affordable or practical. That work can be completed over time or when opportunity presents itself, such as when new developments trigger upgrades to adjacent roadways.

But adapting to our surroundings doesn't mean we have to completely undo our cities. While Toronto has an aggressive replacement and repair program, sometimes the interim (or indeed, complementary) actions are simple. As Oliver Brandes of the POLIS Water Sustainability Project often says, we need to start by thinking like a watershed. Water wants to infiltrate, but paved surfaces prevent it. Where would water go if we didn't have buildings, streets, patios and driveways? How can we integrate our built systems with those natural paths?

The easiest way to reduce some of the strain on current drainage systems is to make use of existing permeable surfaces. Toronto has a bylaw that makes downspout (or roof leader) disconnection mandatory. Disconnecting leaders from sewers reduces the risk of overflows and flooding of bypasses and basements. This preventive measure is so simple that the City's website provides do-it-yourself guidelines, including advice about directing the flow to gardens or lawns, which can readily infiltrate the water into the ground and slow the flow to municipal infrastructure.

Once we've realized the value of our existing natural assets, we can begin to make new permeable surfaces available. My friend Penny suggests having a neighbourhood jackhammer party to break up unwanted patio tiles and celebrate the creation of new green space. On a more official scale, the Toronto-area conservation authorities and municipalities are working hard to make "green" infrastructure more common. In 2009 the city became the first in North America to adopt a bylaw[5] to require green roofs on new commercial, institutional and residential buildings with a gross floor area of 2000 m^2 or more. Progressive building owners and managers take it a step further and find ways to reuse that stormwater within their buildings.

We can also apply the metaphorical jackhammer to parking lots, replacing cement with interlocking brick or permeable pavement that allows infiltration to happen onsite. That's what Credit Valley Conservation did at a number of properties, including the IMAX Corporation headquarters in Mississauga, just west of Toronto. As part of a provincial government program called Showcasing Water Innovation, CVC had received funding to collaborate with public and private partners to demonstrate how Ontario-based technology and expertise could add value to such properties. After the July 8 storm (which heavily impacted the Mississauga area as well), CVC reported that its monitored sites with low-impact development measures in place (another term for green infrastructure) had performed well. Some with permeable pavement installations had slowed the flow to the municipal system by up to 40 minutes, time that allowed the system to recover from the deluge and properly process stormwater. Bioretention planters helped reduce peak flow by almost 50 per cent.

Many projects have proven that investment in adaptive design can not only reduce risk but also help save money in the long run. "It's not just smart from an environmental perspective, it's smart from a capital perspective," says Christine Zimmer, CVC's manager of protection and restoration. "Prior to the summer's extreme events, Mississauga was spending $10-million per year just to maintain and repair erosion control measures on one creek alone. That has nothing to do with extreme events; it's a regular cost. And when you look at existing urban areas, you're limited in controls you can add to a system. Low-impact development can be more easily adopted as part of the existing infrastructure because it requires minimal land expropriation. It also frees up more land for development and property tax revenue."

Mississauga, Toronto and other nearby urban areas are slowly adopting building practices and retrofitting urban structures to acknowledge and work together with the existing natural environment. It's all good work that contributes to slower peak flows, but we can't have an adaptive city until we have something else, namely, buy-in.

When it comes to water and wastewater management, cities are notoriously risk-averse. In Ontario, the Safe Drinking Water Act, 2002 imposes a standard of care on "every person who, on behalf of the municipality, oversees the accredited operating authority of the [drinking water] system or exercises decision-making authority over the system," including municipal councillors and senior staff.

While in most cases cities can install green infrastructure as part of their series of treatment measures at a fraction of the cost of digging up and replacing pipes or installing mammoth holding tanks, many low-impact development practices are still relatively new. CVC is hoping pilot tests and monitored, proven results will be major steps toward general acceptance and use of green infrastructure.

Some municipalities have already accepted these practices and taken a step further, resulting in creativity and even a bit of risk-taking when it comes to revenue models. The City of Kitchener, not 100 kilometres west of Toronto, has moved to a stormwater utility model, charging rates based on a lot's impermeable area. If property owners make an effort to control stormwater – planting and maintaining a rain garden, for instance – they are eligible for credits. The rate revenue funds municipal stormwater projects, and the way lots are measured creates greater equity between the residential and the industrial/commercial/institutional sectors. Assigning a cost to stormwater, like any action that requires end users to pay more into municipal coffers, is a bold move, but it's also a logical one. At the time of writing, consulting firm AECOM had conducted a stormwater financing study on behalf of the City of Mississauga that used Kitchener's success as a case study.[6]

As cities become serious about urban flooding, they can also give property owners incentives to improve their buildings and apply preventive fixes to the costlier design mistakes of the past, such as the plague of reverse-grade driveways in dense suburban neighbourhoods. These driveways are a perfect example of how we ignore the way water behaves. Given there is nothing overland flow loves more than gravity, you have to wonder why this design, which often leads a driveway right into a basement, is so common.

John Kinkead says many of the bungalows built in Mississauga's Cooksville Creek area in the 1950s had carports, not garages, and that homeowners often retrofitted formerly level driveways so they could park in unused basements. While these driveway designs often include catch basins to prevent stormwater from flowing into basements, if the volume of water is overwhelming, storm sewers surcharge and basements, garages and weeping tiles are no longer protected.

In its "Handbook for Reducing Basement Flooding,"[7] the Toronto-based Institute for Catastrophic Loss Reduction suggests installing a backwater valve to prevent surcharges. According to Dan Sandink of ICLR, the cost of installing a backwater valve in a new home is about $150 to $250, while the cost of retrofitting an older home with one can range from $1,000 to $2,000 if not more. In an article for *Canadian Underwriter* magazine, Sandink said several municipalities have implemented programs to help homeowners offset this retrofitting cost, sometimes with programs offering $500 to $3,000 to help homeowners install backwater valves and associated risk reduction measures.[8]

Incentives alone are not going to solve the issue of urban flooding, however. Truly adaptive cities need some major leadership – and while this chapter has highlighted some progressive communities, none are without relationship challenges that can make response time and regulatory changes very slow.

We need leadership

We've already established that cities are susceptible to flood damage precisely because they are cities. There's no shortage of good ideas for handling the urban stormwater issue, but political interests and regulatory red tape can slow momentum. Though conservation authorities are largely responsible for floodplain management in Ontario, their mandate often competes with municipal and development interests.

These days, municipal revenue is a big issue. A September 2012 infrastructure report card[9] estimated the replacement cost for stormwater infrastructure in "fair" to "very poor" condition would be $15.8-billion, or $1,270 per household. If the national infrastructure deficit is pegged at $145-billion, cash-strapped municipalities need to prioritize. According to the report, drinking water and wastewater infrastructure was "good – adequate for now," while municipal roads were "fair – require attention." Overall, the report card rated conditions of stormwater infrastructure across the county to be "very good – fit for the future." Is that a passing grade? If so, what's first on the list for replacement or repairs? Last?

And then there's the development conundrum. You can't run a city without revenue and/or a steady stream of funds from upper-tier governments. Municipal revenue is finite if a city doesn't grow in size or raise taxes. Development charges and subsequent growth in the numbers of property taxpayers can bring in more revenue, but further development usually means more paved surfaces. That said, the complexity of municipal requirements can make or break a development deal. Most developers have traditionally been largely unconcerned with progressive practices; they build to meet code, not exceed it. So if you're a municipality that wants to move beyond the stormwater management status quo, you'll likely have to make some kind of trade-off, because if the municipality next door is offering something more competitive, your vacant greenfield is suddenly less attractive.

Do you risk losing development opportunities to protect constituents and the environment from flood risk, or do you clear the path for developers, collect the property taxes and fund expensive infrastructure projects to protect constituents from increased flood risk?

You can see how these issues are far from cut and dried. The risks posed by a changing climate are not enough to focus municipal efforts, even though flooding damages most infrastructure, including roads and bridges, without bias. So who, besides the municipalities and conservation authorities, is leading the charge?

The insurance industry

In recent years, the Insurance Bureau of Canada has revealed that water-related damage claims now exceed fire damage claims in value. As mentioned earlier, IBC's preliminary estimate of insured property damage after the July 8 storm in the Greater Toronto Area was more than $940-million.

"Beyond what's in the media, the situation is quite dire," says Blair Feltmate, an associate professor of environment at University of Waterloo. "The amount being paid out for property and casualty insurance losses has exceeded the amount coming in the door through premiums in the past few years in Canada. In some places, we may be approaching an uninsurable housing market, which could lead to a hit for the mortgage market – that is, you can't qualify for a mortgage without home insurance."

Feltmate is involved with a Cooperators-initiated program that brings insurers together with the federal government and various premiers and mayors to help governments understand what they need to do to weather-harden infrastructure to help ensure a viable housing market in otherwise flood-vulnerable regions of Canada. (Some would characterize this advocacy as "regulatory capture"; others would say it's just the shot to the arm that decision-makers need to move forward on flood management.)

But municipalities are still finding themselves between a rock and several hard places. After the big summer floods of 2013, mainstream media began to report a call for a federal program to assist provinces with updating floodplain maps – ones that would include provisions for climate change and projected future events. (Recall that Ontario municipalities can set their Regulatory Flood Plains based on regional storms. To truly set a precedent, a city like Toronto, say, could choose to define regulated floodplains based on a more severe storm event – one that is, as in some ways July 8 was, even worse than Hazel.)

Feltmate says that speaking to mayors and

councils about updating floodplain maps is not easy. "Often, they do not want to hear this," he says. Even if past data shows no flooding in potential areas of development, updating maps might indicate red zones and foil building plans that would otherwise yield new property tax revenue. Homeowners in newly designated danger zones can become "snipers in the audience" because their homes might be devalued, he adds. "If you've put a red mark on my home and I can't sell it, it very quickly becomes information I don't want."

Another big issue is the fact that Canada is the only G8 country in which insurance against overland flooding is not available, and that can be very confusing for homeowners.

Etobicoke resident Vivien Fellegi is one such person. On July 8 her basement succumbed to the flood and, as a new and relatively inexperienced homeowner, she wasn't sure what to do. Moreover, she wasn't familiar with her insurance policy.

As a side note, Etobicoke is at the western end of Toronto and was one of the areas hit hardest by the July 8 storm. Etobicoke is bordered on the south by Lake Ontario, on the east by the Humber

River, on the west by Etobicoke Creek and on the north by a large expanse of developed, paved surfaces. Fellegi resides in the federal riding that includes the former lakeshore municipalities of Mimico, New Toronto and Long Branch, an area that suffered major loss during Hurricane Hazel and previous storms. As recently as October 2012, the TRCA published a map that indicates Long Branch is a still flood-vulnerable area.[10]

Shortly after Fellegi moved into her new home about two years ago, she discovered water seeping into her basement, and during the winter of 2012 she learned there were cracks in the foundation. She gathered price quotes for repairs, but due to the freezing temperatures, the work couldn't begin until the spring.

Three weeks after the July 8 storm hit, Fellegi grew tired of waiting for her handyman tenant to fix the basement – in fact, he moved out due to the smell. Because she believed the flooding was her fault – the rain had most likely seeped through the cracks that had yet to be fixed – she hadn't called her insurance company. Few basement remediation companies would give her the time of day. "When I did reach somebody, they weren't sympathetic. 'Thousands of Torontonians have the same problem,' they said. 'Stand in line!'"

"I wanted to cry," Fellegi says. "There was a real panic in me that I wouldn't find a company to get rid of the mould before it ruined the house."

Distraught, she finally called her insurance company as a last resort. As she suspected, when the claims adjuster came to inspect the damage, it didn't look good. But, by a stroke of luck for Fellegi, the inspection revealed debris in the basement drain, indicating a sewer back-up. Under her policy, Fellegi was covered for water damage. Even better, the treatment for water damage and mild mould damage is the same. "Because the drain backed up, I was covered for those two problems," she says. "If the mould had been extensive, that part of the cleanup would be on my dime."

Getting compensated for flooding is complex; to the insurance industry, no two floods are the same. And, as we already know, not many people were as lucky as Fellegi. In September 2013 the Insurance Bureau of Canada announced that the costs of this flood catapulted it to the top of the list of costliest natural disasters in Ontario's history. Some perspective from my co-author, however: by October the flooding in Toronto ranked eighteenth in the national list of hydro-climatic disasters of 2013. Alberta ranked fourth, with an estimated $5.3-billion in damage.

In the months prior to the 2013 Alberta and Toronto floods, Blair Feltmate and co-author Jason Thistlethwaite had explored the viability of overland flood insurance for the Canadian residential property market, interviewing executives from carriers accounting for 57 per cent of the property insurance business in Canada. Their report[11] argued that a viable product could increase revenue for Canadian insurers and also reduce reputational risks associated with uncertainty among homeowners about the types of water damage that are covered. Ultimately, however, what would make overland flood insurance most viable is an environment that encourages risk mitigation – that is, governments that have developed a range of strategies to meet this condition.

Could we really see a collapse of the economy due to flooded basements? You could make that argument, as Feltmate does. Houses and infrastructure aside, however, there are other major risks associated with flooding, and the media almost always misses the mark when it focuses only on the financial costs of structural damage.

Public health risk

Flooding also presents a significant public health risk, but how many people in Toronto received related warnings? Not many, evidently. Two days after the storm, I ran into my friend Steve on the subway. You should know that I consider Steve one of my most intelligent and insightful friends, but when I noticed a beach towel under his arm, I had to second-guess myself about that.

Not only did the July 8 storm send upwards of one billion litres of raw sewage spewing into Lake Ontario, it shot E. coli counts through the roof. According to Lake Ontario Waterkeeper's sample results, counts were well beyond the recreational water quality standards of 100 E. coli per 100 mL of water. At the base of a concrete jungle, Lake Ontario is not the ideal place for a dip after even a rain shower, let alone a torrential downpour. I told Steve as much.

As the editor of a magazine founded in the wake of the Walkerton, Ontario, drinking water tragedy in 2000, it was part of the early days of my job to become acutely aware of the risks posed by E. coli. But should one have to spend a few days deep in the pages of the O'Connor Inquiry report to connect those dots? Granted the episode ultimately changed for the better the way Ontario handles water quality management, but do we need another water-borne public health disaster, this time on the theme of urban flooding?

The next day an email from Steve appeared in my inbox: "Lucky I ran into you yesterday. All things considered, I turned back and had a fine day at home rather than risking storms and E. coli.

Good thing I did, as the levels hit 983 (nearly 40 times higher than my previous swim)!"

Krystyn Tully, vice-president of Lake Ontario Waterkeeper, says there's a missing component to the broader conversation about flooding: the question of risk to public health. When the storm hit, photos of people paddling in the Humber River popped up on social media networks; they seemed unaware they were surrounded by raw sewage. Tully is concerned that Toronto does not currently have a system to alert the public about the health risks storms present.

"People need to be able to make informed decisions about when they go into the water [after a storm]," she says. "There should be a policy that requires the public to be informed when sewage treatment plants are bypassing."

Since Toronto wasn't prepared for the July 8 storm – even sophisticated flood forecast systems didn't catch it in time for people to prepare – there was little that could have been done to notify the public prior to its arrival. During and after the storm, however, we had plenty of warnings about rolling blackouts. The city issued updates as major traffic and transit routes were assessed, repaired and reopened. The TRCA issued a flood warning directed to school boards, municipalities, local conservation authorities, police, emergency services and media. And the irony is not lost in reports of our mayor's brave actions – leaving his car idling in the driveway with its air conditioning blasting to save his family from overheating. A mayor Nenshi he is not, but that's another story.

Interestingly, none of these communications mentioned the potential health hazards posed by contaminated stormwater and raw sewage floating through the streets and watercourses.

A few years ago, Kingston, Ontario, was having serious bypass problems. Using the Environmental Bill of Rights process, Lake Ontario Waterkeeper pressured Kingston to establish a bypass notification policy while the sewage system underwent repairs.

After acquiring the data for Toronto's bypass volumes for July 8, Tully believes the city needs a similar system. "Given the 100-year storms that seem to be happening more often, we can no longer say [these bypasses] are a one-time aberration."

Tully learned a few things from LOW's efforts in Kingston, not the least of which is that the public's attitudes are binary. "The nuance of saying the water is bad one day and good the next is lost. It's hard to make people understand the risks without making them turn their backs on their waterways," says Tully. In other words, we need to create champions of the resource, not enemies. When people come to fear water and lose trust in their municipal systems, even for a second, it is very hard to regain that trust.

Environmental risk

To make people care about urban flooding, you must appeal to what they value. They need to understand the risks to their property and health. But what part do they themselves play in the risk to the environment?

Toronto's paved surfaces not only exacerbate overland flooding, bypasses and overflows, they also contribute to surface runoff and its contamination. If we're expecting to experience wild weather in the future, we can certainly expect to see the impact on the physical, chemical and ecological health of streams, rivers and lakes.[12]

It's already happening and we can see the impact from space. NASA satellite photographs over Lake

Erie and Lake Winnipeg show each summer's record-breaking algal blooms. Experts pin the blame on a combination of urban and agricultural runoff and warming temperatures. Scientists are finding worrisome changes in fish health in the St. Lawrence River, connected to untreated pharmaceuticals from effluent. And in Lake Ontario the latest concern is the proliferation of microplastics that is having a profound impact on ecosystem health.

Toronto's 25-year Wet Weather Flow Master Plan, a $1-billion project underway since 2003, is mapping the future of stormwater control for the city. It includes applying source controls (like the downspout disconnection program), locating and fixing cross-connections, basement flooding protection, water conveyance controls, beach water quality improvements, stream and aquatic habitat restoration, end-of-pipe facilities, and monitoring.

In reference to the plan, Abe Khademi says reducing reliance on hard infrastructure gives cities more adaptability to design for changing climate. But Tully says the plan isn't ambitious enough. "It's not a plan to clean up Toronto's waterways, it's a plan to pollute them less," she says. "In a perfect world, it would be an infrastructure plan connected to a broader policy vision for what the city should be, but doing something is better than doing nothing. The plan is happening, it needs to happen, but it doesn't solve the whole problem and it's really the minimum we should be doing."

We must make a place for flooding to happen

Before he spoke at the 2013 Columbia Basin Watershed Network Symposium, Canadian public intellectual and author John Ralston Saul told me in an interview[13] he'd been rethinking the relationship we have with place.

"As Canadians, we've taken this view that humans are on top and everything is here to serve us, but it doesn't work that way," he said.

> Canada has a long history of benefiting from its commodities and convincing ourselves that we're smart as opposed to lucky. We have fished, mined, polluted – you name it, we've done it – as if we have the right to do it, and moved on. Are we able to accept that we were extremely lucky to get a place with all of these commodities, and that to be successful we have to respect these commodities

> rather than cash in? We have to learn that commodity-rich countries succeed only when they understand the relationship between people and place, and [that] ease of making short-term benefit from these commodities is a destructive delusion. We have to make proper use of our role.

Hearing those remarks, I couldn't help but draw parallels to urban flooding. How does it reflect the relationship Torontonians have with their surroundings?

In building cities, we have largely ignored the natural flow. In Toronto we've buried entire rivers and built neighbourhoods on top of them like they never existed. We take our drinking water from Lake Ontario and at the same time use the lake as a repository for our treated waste and, more passively, our contaminated stormwater, whether short shower or torrential downpour.

Back to Burtynsky, the photographer of human systems. In an interview about his recent *Water* series, he told me what he learned during his five-year study of the resource. "While water is forgiving and can rehabilitate, it's not infinitely resilient."[14] At what point does the lake reach its tipping point? As the insurance dilemma shows, it might be when we start to see the threat flooding poses to our prosperity. Right now, that means flooded basements, so we engineer solutions to avoid that problem. In a "new normal" future, however, could it mean a real threat to our water supply? What effect would that have on our Western understanding of prosperity?

John Ralston Saul had more to add, from the interview cited earlier:

> [Economics] is a social phenomenon. It's about how we want to live and how we should go about it. It has always been that. The last 40 years have been about pretending that economics had their own truth and you could impose that truth on human beings and society, even if it was destructive. The next big question will be whether or not we've learned from that.

At the root of our approach to urban flooding, it seems, is a set of just such questions. How do we want to live? Do we want to continue pursuing the same notion of economy, the success of which, by the way, rests entirely on the health and availability of our water? And where exactly does a healthy environment fit into the picture?

While it seems logical to say we should endeavour to respect and protect the waterways that make our lives and cities possible, the majority of the time we bury this responsibility like our rivers, allowing it to surface only during times of emergency or when it affects the bottom line.

Municipalities worry about revenue and try to attract developers so they can grow their property tax base. Insurance companies want to see municipalities spend funds on protecting themselves and their constituents from flooded property so that insurance claims will go down. Homeowners want to know their assets are safe from being devalued and that municipalities are not wasting their tax dollars. In navigating these choppy cross-currents, we rarely stop to think about the long-term impacts.

Who decides how to manage this risk? I don't have that answer. I'm not sure anyone does. But I do know more focused work could put Toronto on the road to resilience. Conservation authorities, and to a similar extent the City, realize we can't do much to stop the storms from coming, but we can be better prepared to handle them.

We must adopt whole-system thinking and create useful, directive policies with clear language and expected outcomes. We must also adapt our existing systems. Throwing money at flooded basements does not solve the problem, and short of ripping up and replacing all our pipes, we can never fully remove flood risk. But we can "slow the flow" with green infrastructure projects and work toward capturing and treating stormwater before we release it into Lake Ontario.

With the knowledge that the environment fuels the economy (and not the other way around), we can think bigger than just protecting basements. For instance, could we feasibly "daylight" some of our buried urban watercourses to prevent rain from entering the sewer system? Even better, could we move to a localized urban system that doesn't require sewers at all? Dutch scientist Grietje Zeeman works in this space and sees "new sanitation" – wastewater separated at the source, recycled and returned to the system – as the future. Can we envision a world without bypasses and overflows, or is it too difficult for cities to see past sunk capital?

True resilience is not just about weathering a storm; it's about a new collective mindset. As Lake Ontario Waterkeeper's Krystyn Tully asks, can we figure out how to run a city and respect the waterway that supports it? Can we make a place for flooding to happen?

When we develop land, we need to demand smarter design and hold the developers accountable. City plans need to include more places for flooding to happen. Unlike Marie Curtis Park in Long Branch, which honours the people who lost homes and relatives to Hazel, and the reeve who came to their aid, parks should not be built in tribute to victims of disaster; they should celebrate and respect natural systems. They should be symbols of progress. They should encourage recreation and bring people closer to water.

Finally, we need to act, and soon. It took three major storms, including Hazel – and untold loss – for Toronto to decide to turn part of Long Branch into Marie Curtis Park. We've learned since then, but we still experience events that lead to great loss. At what point do we understand the risks, demand action and make the move to truly resilient cities?

Endnotes

1 Hugh Mackenzie, "Canada's Infrastructure Gap: Where it came from and why it will cost so much to close," (Ottawa: Canadian Centre for Policy Alternatives, January 2013), 6, accessed 2014-02-04 (pdf) from www.policyalternatives.ca/publications/reports/canadas-infrastructure-gap.

2 Ecojustice.ca, "The Great Lakes Sewage Report Card," (Vancouver: August 2013), 6, accessed 2014-02-04 (pdf) from www.ecojustice.ca/publications/the-great-lakes-sewage-report-card-2013.

3 David J. Nowak et al., "Assessing Urban Forest Effects and Values: Toronto's Urban Forest," Resource Bulletin NRS-79 (Newtown Square, Pa.: US Department of Agriculture, Forest Service, Northern Research Station, May 2013), 9, accessed 2014-02-04 (pdf), www.nrs.fs.fed.us/pubs/rb/rb_nrs79.pdf.

4 Ontario Ministry of Infrastructure, "Growth Plan for the Greater Golden Horseshoe, 2006, 2012," (Toronto), 12, 16 [pdf 13, 17], accessed 2014-02-04, www.placestogrow.ca/content/ggh/plan-cons-english-all-web.pdf.

5 City of Toronto, "Toronto Green Roof Bylaw," webpage, n.d., accessed 2014-02-04, http://is.gd/lmeoca.

6 AECOM Canada Ltd., "Stormwater Financing Study," prepared for the City of Mississauga (Kitchener, Ont.: AECOM Canada Ltd., April 2013), 30–32, accessed 2014-02-04 (pdf), www7.mississauga.ca/Documents/TW/Environment/RPT_MississaugaStormwaterFinancingStudy_Apr2013_Final.pdf.

7 Institute for Catastrophic Loss Reduction, "Handbook for Reducing Basement Flooding," (Toronto: n.d.), accessed 2014-02-08 (pdf) from www.basementfloodreduction.com/forhomeowners/20tipsforhomeowners.html.

8 "Open to Interpretation," *Canadian Underwriter*, July 2013, accessed 2014-02-08, www.canadianunderwriter.ca/news/open-to-interpretation/1002489855.

9 Canadian Society for Civil Engineering et al., "Canadian Infrastructure Report Card, 2012," accessed 2014-02-08 (pdf) from www.canadainfrastructure.ca. See also Kerry Freek and Mira Shenker, "The State of Our Water Assets: Experts Comment on Canada's First Municipal Infrastructure Report Card," *Water Canada* online, posted 2012-11-16, accessed 2014-02-04, http://watercanada.net/2012/the-state-of-our-water-assets.

10 Toronto and Region Conservation Authority, "Flood Vulnerable Areas" (map), (Downsview, Ont.: October 2012), accessed 2014-02-08 (pdf) from http://is.gd/hpMnID.

11 Jason Thistlethwaite and Blair Feltmate, "Assessing the Viability of Overland Flood Insurance: The Canadian Residential Property Market," (Guelph, Ont.: The Cooperators, September 2013), accessed 2014-02-04 (pdf)

from final paragraph at www.cooperators.ca/en/About-Us/about-sustainability/extreme-weather-and-insurance.aspx.

12 Toronto and Region Conservation Authority, "Meeting the Challenge of Climate Change: TRCA Action Plan for the Living City," (Downsview, Ont.: n.d.), accessed 2014-02-04 (pdf), www.trca.on.ca/dotAsset/16642.pdf.

13 Kerry Freek, "Interview: John Ralston Saul on Environment, Economics, Governance and First Nations," *Water Canada* online, posted 2013-09-23, accessed 2014-02-04, http://watercanada.net/2013/interview-john-ralston-saul-on-environment-economics-governance-and-first-nations.

14 Kerry Freek, "Massive Public Shift: Can Edward Burtynsky's photographs motivate a global attitude adjustment?" *Water Canada 13*, no. 5 (September/October 2013), 16, accessed 2014-02-04, http://watercanada.net/2013/massive-public-shift.

Further reading

AECOM Canada Ltd. "Stormwater Financing Study." Prepared for the City of Mississauga. Kitchener, Ont.: (April 2013): 30–32. Accessed 2014-02-04 (pdf), www7.mississauga.ca/Documents/TW/Environment/RPT_MississaugaStormwaterFinancingStudy_Apr2013_Final.pdf.

Bakker, Karen, ed. *Eau Canada: The Future of Canada's Water.* Vancouver: UBC Press, 2007.

Bazerman, Max H., and Michael D. Watkins. *Predictable Surprises: The Disasters You Should Have Seen Coming and How To Prevent Them*. Boston: Harvard Business School Press, 2004.

Bergkamp, Ger, and Claudia W. Sadoff. "Water in a Sustainable Economy," ch. 8 in *2008 State of the World: Innovations for a Sustainable Economy*. 25th Anniv. Edition, edited by Gary T. Gardner, Thomas Prugh, Linda Starke and Worldwatch Institute. New York, London: W.W. Norton, 2008.

Brooks, David, Oliver Brandes and Stephen Gurman, eds. "Avoiding the Perfect Storm: Weathering Climate Change by Following Its Effects on Water Resources." In *Making the Most of the Water We Have: The Soft Path Approach to Water Management*. Sterling, Va.: Earthscan, 2009.

Bruce, James B., et al. "The Sustainable Management of Groundwater in Canada." Report of the Expert Panel on Groundwater. Ottawa: Council of Canadian Academies, 2009. Accessed 2014-02-01 (pdf) from http://is.gd/mlHNjC.

Canadian Society for Civil Engineering et al. "Canadian Infrastructure Report Card, 2012." Accessed 2014-02-08 (pdf) from www.canadainfrastructure.ca.

City of Toronto. "Toronto Green Roof Bylaw." Webpage (n.d.). Accessed 2014-02-04, http://is.gd/lmeoca.

Conca, Ken. *Governing Water: Contentious Transnational Politics and Global Institution Building.* Cambridge, Mass.: MIT Press, 2006.

Cullen, Heidi. *The Weather of the Future: Heat Waves, Extreme Storms and Other Scenes from a Climate-Changed Planet.* New York: HarperCollins, 2010.

de Loë, R.C. "Toward a Canadian National Water Strategy." Prepared for Canadian Water Resources Assn. Guelph, Ont.: Rob de Loë Consulting Services, 2008. Accessed 2014-02-01 (pdf) from http://is.gd/X6JimS.

Ecojustice.ca. "The Great Lakes Sewage Report Card." Vancouver: August 2013, 6. Accessed 2014-02-04 (pdf) from www.ecojustice.ca/publications/the-great-lakes-sewage-report-card-2013.

Farrell, Lauren, et al. "Storm of August 19, 2005: A Catalyst for Change from Reactive to Adaptive Urban Flood Management in Toronto, Ontario, Canada." International Symposium on Flood Defence, Toronto, May 6–8, 2008.

Freek, Kerry. "Massive Public Shift: Can Edward Burtynsky's Photographs Motivate a Global Attitude Adjustment?" *Water Canada 13*, no. 5 (September/October 2013): 16. Accessed 2014-02-04, http://watercanada.net/2013/massive-public-shift.

———. "Interview: John Ralston Saul on Environment, Economics, Governance and First Nations." *Water Canada* online, posted 2013-09-23. Accessed 2014-02-04, http://watercanada.net/2013/interview-john-ralston-saul-on-environment-economics-governance-and-first-nations.

Freek, Kerry, and Mira Shenker. "The State of Our Water Assets: Experts Comment on Canada's First Municipal Infrastructure Report Card." *Water Canada* online, posted 2012-11-16. Accessed 2014-02-04, http://watercanada.net/2012/the-state-of-our-water-assets.

Garvey, James. *The Ethics of Climate Change: Right and Wrong in a Warming World*. New York: Continuum, 2008.

Hansen, James. *Storms of My Grandchildren: The Truth about the Coming Climate Catastrophe and Our Last Chance to Save Humanity*. New York: Bloomsbury Press, 2009.

Hewitt, Kenneth, and Ian Burton. *The Hazardousness of a Place: A Regional Ecology of Damaging Events*. Toronto: University of Toronto Press, 1971.

Ingram, Helen. "Beyond Universal Remedies for Good Water Governance: A Political and Contextual Approach." Presented at the Sixth Biennial Rosenberg International Forum on Water Policy, Zaragoza, Spain, 2008. Accessed 2014-02-01 (pdf) from http://is.gd/Smw9g9.

Institute for Catastrophic Loss Reduction. "Handbook for Reducing Basement Flooding." Toronto: n.d. Accessed 2014-02-08 (pdf) from www.basementfloodreduction.com/forhomeowners/20tipsforhomeowners.html.

Mackenzie, Hugh. "Canada's Infrastructure Gap: Where it Came from and Why It Will Cost So Much to Close." Ottawa: Canadian Centre for Policy Alternatives (January 2013): 6. Accessed 2014-02-04 (pdf) from www.policyalternatives.ca/publications/reports/canadas-infrastructure-gap.

Mann, Michael E. *The Hockey Stick and the Climate Wars: Dispatches from the Front Lines*. New York: Columbia University Press, 2012.

Nowak, David J., et al. "Assessing Urban Forest Effects and Values: Toronto's Urban Forest." Resource Bulletin NRS-79. Newtown Square, Pa.: US Department of Agriculture, Forest Service, Northern Research Station (May 2013): 9. Accessed 2014-02-04 (pdf), www.nrs.fs.fed.us/pubs/rb/rb_nrs79.pdf.

Ontario Ministry of Infrastructure. "Growth Plan for the Greater Golden Horseshoe, 2006, 2012." (Toronto): 12, 16 [pdf 13, 17]. Accessed 2014-02-04, www.placestogrow.ca/content/ggh/plan-cons-english-all-web.pdf.

Pentland, Ralph, and Chris Wood. *Down the Drain: How We Are Failing to Protect Our Water Resources*. Vancouver: Greystone Books, 2013.

Sandford, Robert W. *Restoring the Flow: Confronting the World's Water Woes*. Calgary: Rocky Mountain Books, 2009.

———. *Water, Weather and the Mountain West.* Calgary: Rocky Mountain Books, 2007.

Sandford, Robert W., and Merrell-Ann S. Phare. *Ethical Water: Learning to Value What Matters Most.* Calgary: Rocky Mountain Books, 2011.

Sandford, Robert W., and Steve Short. *Water and Our Way of Life.* Fernie, BC: Rockies Network, 2003.

Sandink, Dan. "Open to Interpretation" [re residential backwater valves], *Canadian Underwriter* (July 2013). Accessed 2014-02-08, www.canadianunderwriter.ca/news/open-to-interpretation/1002489855.

Thistlethwaite, Jason, and Blair Feltmate. "Assessing the Viability of Overland Flood Insurance: The Canadian Residential Property Market." Guelph, Ont.: The Cooperators, September 2013. Accessed 2014-02-08 (pdf) from final paragraph at www.cooperators.ca/en/About-Us/about-sustainability/extreme-weather-and-insurance.aspx.

Toronto and Region Conservation Authority. "Flood Vulnerable Areas" (map). Downsview, Ont.: October 2012. Accessed 2014-02-08 (pdf) from http://is.gd/hpMnID.

———. "Meeting the Challenge of Climate Change: TRCA Action Plan for the Living City." Downsview, Ont.: Toronto and Region Conservation Authority, n.d. Accessed 2014-02-04 (pdf), www.trca.on.ca/dotAsset/16642.pdf.

The RMB manifestos

PASSIONATE. PROVOCATIVE. POPULIST.

RMB has created one of the most unique non-fiction series in Canadian publishing. The books in this collection are meant to be literary, critical and cultural studies that are provocative, passionate and populist in nature. The goal is to encourage debate and help facilitate positive change whenever and wherever possible. Books in this uniquely packaged hardcover series are limited to a length of of 20,000–25,000 words. They're enlightening to read and attractive to hold.

ISBN 978-1-927330-80-7

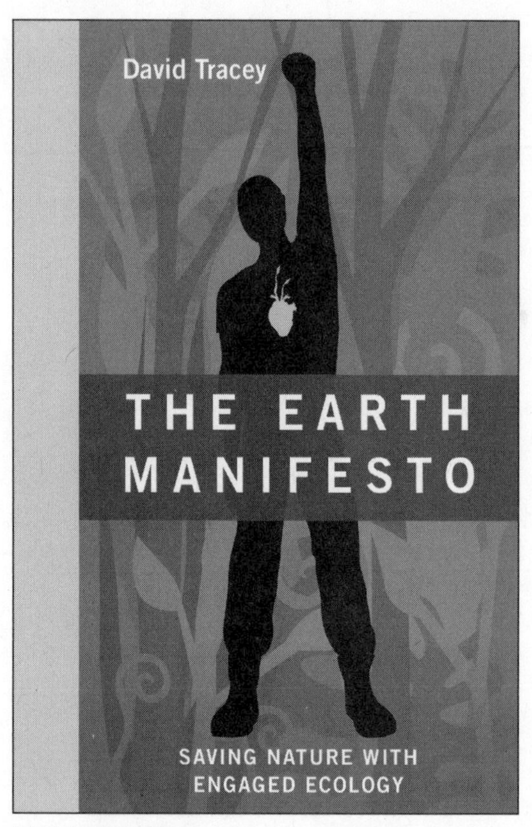

ISBN 978-1-927330-89-0

ISBN 978-1-927330-83-8

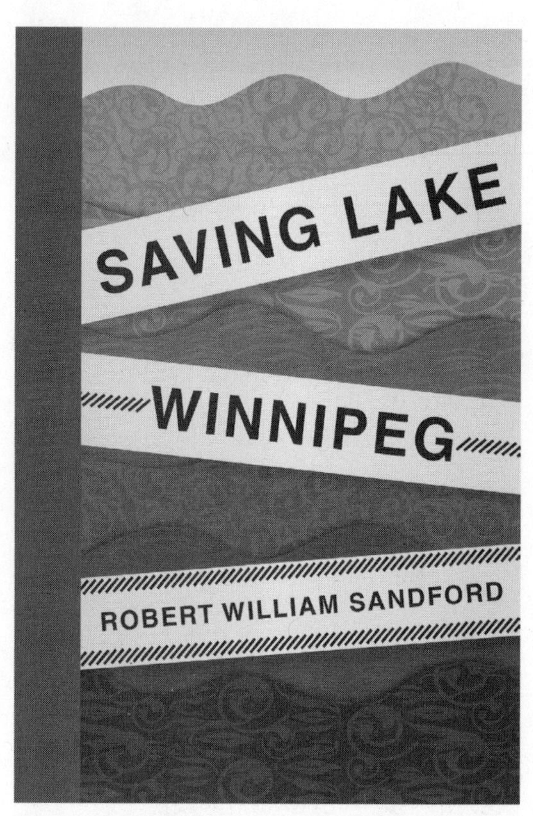

ISBN 978-1-927330-86-9

ISBN 978-1-926855-68-4

ISBN 978-1-927330-21-0

gift ECOLOGY

PETER DENTON

ISBN 978-1-927330-40-1

The
INSATIABLE
Bark
Beetle

Dr. Reese Halter

ISBN 978-1-926855-67-7

ISBN 978-1-926855-65-3

ISBN 978-1-926855-58-5

ISBN 978-1-897522-83-7

ISBN 978-1-926855-72-1

Ethical Water

LEARNING TO VALUE WHAT MATTERS MOST

Robert William Sandford and Merrell-Ann S. Phare

ISBN 978-1-926855-70-7

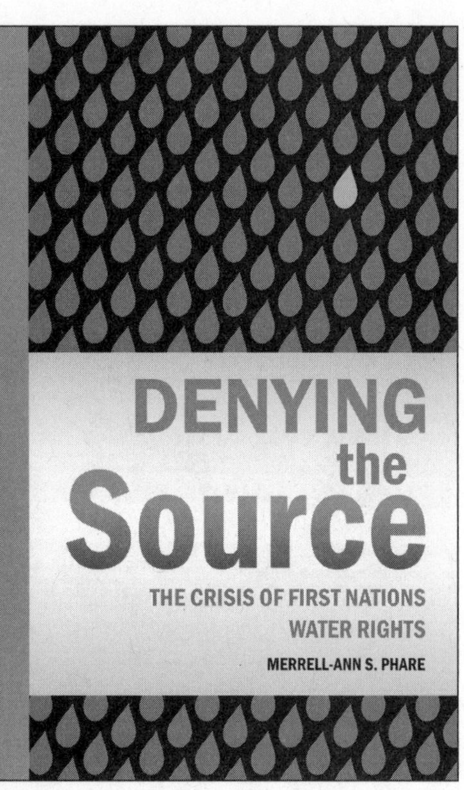

ISBN 978-1-897522-61-5

ISBN 978-1-897522-10-3

RMB saved the following resources by printing the pages of this book on chlorine-free paper made with 100% post-consumer waste:

Trees · 8, fully grown
Water · 3,680 gallons
Energy · 4 million BTUs
Solid Waste · 246 pounds
Greenhouse Gases · 678 pounds

CALCULATIONS BASED ON RESEARCH BY ENVIRONMENTAL DEFENSE AND THE PAPER TASK FORCE. MANUFACTURED AT FRIESENS CORPORATION.